# www.EffortlessMath.com

... So Much More Online!

✓ FREE Math lessons

✓ More Math learning books!

✓ Mathematics Worksheets

✓ Online Math Tutors

**Need a PDF version of this book?**

Please visit www.EffortlessMath.com

# CLEP College Algebra Study Guide 2020 - 2021

*A Comprehensive Review and Step-By-Step Guide to Preparing for the CLEP College Algebra*

By

Reza Nazari

All inquiries should be addressed to:

info@effortlessMath.com

www.EffortlessMath.com

**ISBN:** 978-1-64612-924-9

**Published by: Effortless Math Education**

**www.EffortlessMath.com**

**Visit www.EffortlessMath.com**

**for Online Math Practice**

## Description

***CLEP College Algebra Study Guide***, which reflects the 2020 - 2021 test guidelines, is designed by top College Algebra instructors and test prep experts to help test takers succeed on the CLEP College Algebra Test. The updated version of this comprehensive CLEP College Algebra preparation book includes Math lessons, extensive exercises, sample College Algebra questions, and quizzes with answers and detailed solutions to help you hone your math skills, overcome your exam anxiety, boost your confidence—and do your best to ace the CLEP College Algebra exam on test day. Upon completion of this perfect CLEP College Algebra prep book, you will have a solid foundation and sufficient practice to ace the CLEP College Algebra test.

Not only does this all-inclusive prep book offer everything you will ever need to prepare for the CLEP College Algebra test, but it also contains two complete and realistic CLEP College Algebra tests that reflect the format and question types on the CLEP College Algebra to help you check your exam-readiness and identify where you need more practice.

***CLEP College Algebra Study Guide*** contains many exciting and unique features to help you prepare for the CLEP College Algebra test, including:

- ✓ Content 100% aligned with the 2020 CLEP College Algebra test
- ✓ Written by CLEP College Algebra instructors and test experts
- ✓ Complete coverage of all CLEP College Algebra concepts and topics which you will be tested
- ✓ Step-by-step guide for all CLEP College Algebra topics
- ✓ Abundant Math skill building exercises to help test-takers approach different question types that might be unfamiliar to them
- ✓ Exercises on different College Algebra topics such as integers, percent, equations, polynomials, exponents and radicals
- ✓ 2 full-length practice tests (featuring new question types) with detailed answers

This CLEP College Algebra prep book and other Effortless Math Education books are used by thousands of students each year to help them review core content areas, brush-up in math, discover their strengths and weaknesses, and achieve their best scores on the CLEP College Algebra test.

## Contents

| Name: ................................................ | Date: ........................................................ |
|---|---|

| **Topic** | **Adding and Subtracting Integers** |
|---|---|
| **Notes** | ✓ Integers include: zero, counting numbers, and the negative of the counting numbers $\{\ ,-3,-2,-1,0,1,2,3,...\}$<br>✓ Add a positive integer by moving to the right on the number line.<br>✓ Add a negative integer by moving to the left on the number line. Subtract an integer by adding its opposite. |
| **Examples** | ***Solve.*** $(4)-(-8)=$<br>Keep the first number and convert the sign of the second number to its opposite. (change subtraction into addition. Then: $(4)+8=12$<br><br>***Solve.*** $42+(12-26)=$<br>First subtract the numbers in brackets, $12-26=-14$<br>Then: $42+(-14)= \ \rightarrow$ change addition into subtraction: $42-14=28$ |
| **Your Turn!** | 1) $-(15)+12=$ <br><br> 2) $(-2)+(-10)+18=$ <br><br> 3) $(-13)+7=$ <br><br> 4) $3-(-7)+14=$ <br><br> 5) $(-7)+(-8)=$ <br><br> 6) $16-(-4+8)=$ <br><br> 7) $4+(-15)+2=$ <br><br> 8) $-(22)-(-4)+8=$ |

| Name: ........................................................... | Date: ........................................................... |
|---|---|

| Topic | **Adding and Subtracting Integers - Answers** | |
|---|---|---|
| **Notes** | ✓ Integers include: zero, counting numbers, and the negative of the counting numbers. $\{\ldots, -3, -2, -1, 0, 1, 2, 3, \ldots\}$<br>✓ Add a positive integer by moving to the right on the number line.<br>✓ Add a negative integer by moving to the left on the number line.<br>Subtract an integer by adding its opposite. | |
| **Examples** | **Solve.** $(4) - (-8) =$<br>Keep the first number and convert the sign of the second number to its opposite. (change subtraction into addition. Then: $(4) + 8 = 12$<br><br>**Solve.** $42 + (12 - 26) =$<br>First subtract the numbers in brackets, $12 - 26 = -14$<br>Then: $42 + (-14) = \rightarrow$ change addition into subtraction: $42 - 14 = 28$ | |
| **Your Turn!** | 1) $-(15) + 12 = -3$ | 2) $(-2) + (-10) + 18 = 6$ |
| | 3) $(-13) + 7 = -6$ | 4) $3 - (-7) + 14 = 24$ |
| | 5) $(-7) + (-8) = -15$ | 6) $16 - (-4 + 8) = 12$ |
| | 7) $4 + (-15) + 2 = -9$ | 8) $(-22) - (-4) + 8 = -10$ |

| Name: ........................................ | Date: ........................................ |
|---|---|

| Topic | **Multiplying and Dividing Integers** |
|---|---|
| **Notes** | Use following rules for multiplying and dividing integers:<br><br>✓ (negative) × (negative) = positive<br>✓ (negative) ÷ (negative) = positive<br>✓ (negative) × (positive) = negative<br>✓ (negative) ÷ (positive) = negative<br>✓ (positive) × (positive) = positive<br>✓ (positive) ÷ (negative) = negative |
| **Examples** | **Solve**. $2 \times (14 - 17) =$<br>First subtract the numbers in brackets, $14 - 17 = -3 \rightarrow (2) \times (-3) =$<br>Now use this rule: (positive) × (negative) = negative<br>$(2) \times (-3) = -6$<br><br>**Solve**. $(-7) + (-36 \div 4) =$<br>First divide $-36$ by $4$, the numbers in brackets, using this rule:<br>(negative) ÷ (positive) = negative<br>Then: $-36 \div 4 = -9$. Now, add $-7$ and $-9$:<br>$$(-7) + (-9) = -7 - 9 = -16$$ |

| | | |
|---|---|---|
| **Your Turn!** | 1) $(-7) \times 6 =$ | 2) $(-63) \div (-7) =$ |
| | 3) $(-11) \times (-3) =$ | 4) $81 \div (-9) =$ |
| | 5) $(15 - 12) \times (-7) =$ | 6) $(-12) \div (3) =$ |
| | 7) $4 \times (-9) =$ | 8) $(8) \div (-2) =$ |

| Name: .................................... | Date: ............................................. |
|---|---|

| Topic | **Multiplying and Dividing Integers - Answers** ||
|---|---|---|
| **Notes** | Use following rules for multiplying and dividing integers: <br><br> ✓ (negative) × (negative) = positive <br> ✓ (negative) ÷ (negative) = positive <br> ✓ (negative) × (positive) = negative <br> ✓ (negative) ÷ (positive) = negative <br> ✓ (positive) × (positive) = positive <br> ✓ (positive) ÷ (negative) = negative ||
| **Examples** | **Solve.** $2 \times (14 - 17) =$ <br> First subtract the numbers in brackets, $14 - 17 = -3 \rightarrow (2) \times (-3) =$ <br> Now use this rule: (positive) × (negative) = negative <br> $(2) \times (-3) = -6$ <br><br> **Solve.** $(-7) + (-36 \div 4) =$ <br> First divide $-36$ by $4$, the numbers in brackets, using this rule: <br> (negative) ÷ (positive) = negative <br> Then: $-36 \div 4 = -9$. Now, add $-7$ and $-9$: <br> $(-7) + (-9) = -7 - 9 = -16$ ||
| **Your Turn!** | 1) $(-7) \times 6 = -42$ | 2) $(-63) \div (-7) = 9$ |
| | 3) $(-11) \times (-3) = 33$ | 4) $81 \div (-9) = -9$ |
| | 5) $(15 - 12) \times (-7) = -21$ | 6) $(-12) \div (3) = -4$ |
| | 7) $4 \times (-9) = -36$ | 8) $(8) \div (-2) = -4$ |

| Name: ............................... | Date: ................................ |
|---|---|

| **Topic** | **Order of Operation** |
|---|---|
| **Notes** | When there is more than one math operation, use PEMDAS: <br> (to memorize this rule, remember the phrase "Please Excuse My Dear Aunt Sally") <br><br> ✓ Parentheses <br><br> ✓ Exponents <br><br> ✓ Multiplication and Division (from left to right) <br><br> ✓ Addition and Subtraction (from left to right) |
| **Examples** | ***Calculate.*** $(18 - 26) \div (2^4 \div 4) =$ <br><br> First simplify inside parentheses: $(-8) \div (16 \div 4) = (-8) \div (4)$ <br> Then: $(-8) \div (4) = -2$ <br><br> ***Solve.*** $(-5 \times 7) - (18 - 3^2) -$ <br><br> First calculate within parentheses: $(-5 \times 7) - (18 - 3^2) = (-35) - (18 - 9)$ <br> Then: $(-35) - (18 - 9) = -35 - 9 = -44$ |

<table>
<tr><td rowspan="4">Your Turn!</td><td>1) $(11 \times 4) \div (5 + 6) =$</td><td>2) $(30 \div 5) + (17 - 8) =$</td></tr>
<tr><td>3) $(-9) + (5 \times 6) + 14 =$</td><td>4) $(-10 \times 5) \div (2^2 + 1) =$</td></tr>
<tr><td>5) $[-16(32 \div 2^3)] \div 8 =$</td><td>6) $(-7) + (72 \div 3^2) + 12 =$</td></tr>
<tr><td>7) $[16(32 \div 2^3)] - 4^2 =$</td><td>8) $4^3 + (-5 \times 2^5) + 5 =$</td></tr>
</table>

| Name: .................................. | Date: ........................................... |
|---|---|

| Topic | Order of Operation - Answers | |
|---|---|---|
| **Notes** | When there is more than one math operation, use PEMDAS:<br>(to memorize this rule, remember the phrase "Please Excuse My Dear Aunt Sally")<br>✓ Parentheses<br><br>✓ Exponents<br><br>✓ Multiplication and Division (from left to right)<br><br>✓ Addition and Subtraction (from left to right) | |
| **Examples** | ***Calculate.*** $(18 - 26) \div (2^4 \div 4) =$ <br><br>First simplify inside parentheses: $(-8) \div (16 \div 4) = (-8) \div (4)$<br>Then: $(-8) \div (4) = -2$ <br><br>***Solve.*** $(-5 \times 7) - (18 - 3^2) =$ <br><br>First calculate within parentheses: $(-5 \times 7) - (18 - 3^2) = (-35) - (18 - 9)$<br>Then: $(-35) - (18 - 9) = -35 - 9 = -44$ | |
| **Your Turn!** | 1) $(11 \times 4) \div (5 + 6) = 4$ | 2) $(30 \div 5) + (17 - 8) = 15$ |
| | 3) $(-9) + (5 \times 6) + 14 =$ <br><br>$35$ | 4) $(-10 \times 5) \div (2^2 + 1) = -10$ |
| | 5) $[-16(32 \div 2^3)] \div 8 =$ <br><br>$-8$ | 6) $(-7) + (72 \div 3^2) + 12 = 13$ |
| | 7) $[16(32 \div 2^3)] - 4^2 =$ <br><br>$48$ | 8) $4^3 + (-5 \times 2^5) + 5 = \quad 91$ |

| Name: .................................................. | Date: ............................................................. |
|---|---|

| **Topic** | **Integers and Absolute Value** |
|---|---|
| **Notes** | ✓ The absolute value of a number is its distance from zero, in either direction, on the number line. For example, the distance of 9 and $-9$ from zero on number line is 9.<br><br>✓ Absolute value is symbolized by vertical bars, as in $\|x\|$. |
| **Example** | ***Calculate.*** $\|8-5\| \times \|12-16\| =$<br><br>First calculate $\|8-5\|$, $\to \|8-5\| = \|3\|$, the absolute value of 3 is 3, $\|3\| = 3$<br><br>$8 \times \|12-16\| =$<br><br>Now calculate $\|12-16\|$, $\to \|12-16\| = \|-4\|$, the absolute value of $-4$ is 4, $\|-4\| = 4$. Then: $3 \times 4 = 12$ |

| **Your Turn!** | 1) $11 - \|4-13\| =$ | 2) $14 - \|12-19\| - \|9\| =$ |
|---|---|---|
| | 3) $\|21\| - \dfrac{\|-25\|}{5} =$ | 4) $\|30\| + \dfrac{\|-49\|}{7} =$ |
| | 5) $\dfrac{\|7 \times -8\|}{4} \times \dfrac{\|-12\|}{2} =$ | 6) $\dfrac{\|10 \times -6\|}{5} \times \|-9\| =$ |
| | 7) $\dfrac{\|-20\|}{5} \times \dfrac{\|-36\|}{6} =$ | 8) $\|-30+6\| \times \dfrac{\|-9 \times 4\|}{12} =$ |

| Name: .......................................... | Date: .......................................... |

| Topic | **Integers and Absolute Value - Answers** | |
|---|---|---|
| **Notes** | ✓ The absolute value of a number is its distance from zero, in either direction, on the number line. For example, the distance of 9 and $-9$ from zero on number line is 9. <br><br> ✓ Absolute value is symbolized by vertical bars, as in $\lvert x \rvert$. | |
| **Example** | **Calculate.** $\lvert 8 - 5 \rvert \times \lvert 12 - 16 \rvert =$ <br><br> First calculate $\lvert 8 - 5 \rvert$, $\rightarrow \lvert 8 - 5 \rvert = \lvert 3 \rvert$, the absolute value of 3 is 3, $\lvert 3 \rvert = 3$ <br><br> $8 \times \lvert 12 - 16 \rvert =$ <br><br> Now calculate $\lvert 12 - 16 \rvert$, $\rightarrow \lvert 12 - 16 \rvert = \lvert -4 \rvert$, the absolute value of $-4$ is 4, $\lvert -4 \rvert = 4$. Then: $3 \times 4 = 12$ | |
| **Your Turn!** | 1) $11 - \lvert 4 - 13 \rvert = 2$ | 2) $14 - \lvert 12 - 19 \rvert - \lvert 9 \rvert = -2$ |
| | 3) $\lvert 21 \rvert - \dfrac{\lvert -25 \rvert}{5} = 16$ | 4) $\lvert 30 \rvert + \dfrac{\lvert -49 \rvert}{7} = 37$ |
| | 5) $\dfrac{\lvert 7 \times -8 \rvert}{4} \times \dfrac{\lvert -12 \rvert}{2} = 84$ | 6) $\dfrac{\lvert 10 \times -6 \rvert}{5} \times \lvert -9 \rvert = 108$ |
| | 7) $\dfrac{\lvert -20 \rvert}{5} \times \dfrac{\lvert -36 \rvert}{6} = 24$ | 8) $\lvert -30 + 6 \rvert \times \dfrac{\lvert -9 \times 4 \rvert}{12} = 72$ |

| Name: ........................... | Date: ................................... |
|---|---|

| **Topic** | **Simplifying Variable Expressions** |
|---|---|
| **Notes** | ✓ In algebra, a variable is a letter used to stand for a number. The most common letters are: $x, y, z, a, b, c, m,$ and $n$.<br>✓ Algebraic expression is an expression contains integers, variables, and the math operations such as addition, subtraction, multiplication, division, etc.<br>✓ In an expression, we can combine "like" terms. (values with same variable and same power) |
| **Example** | ***Simplify this expression***. $(6x + 8x + 9) =?$<br>Combine like terms. Then: $(6x + 8x + 4) = 14x + 9$<br>**(remember you cannot combine variables and numbers).** |

| **Your Turn!** | 1) $5x + 2 - 2x =$ | 2) $4 + 7x + 3x =$ |
|---|---|---|
| | 3) $8x + 3 - 3x =$ | 4) $-2 - x^2 - 6x^2 =$ |
| | 5) $3 + 10x^2 + 2 =$ | 6) $8x^2 + 6x + 7x^2 =$ |
| | 7) $5x^2 - 12x^2 + 8x =$ | 8) $2x^2 - 2x - x + 5x^2 =$ |
| | 9) $4x - (12 - 30x) =$ | 10)  $10x - (80x - 48) =$ |

| Name: ............................................. | Date: ........................................... |
|---|---|

| Topic | **Simplifying Variable Expressions - Answers** |
|---|---|
| **Notes** | ✓ In algebra, a variable is a letter used to stand for a number. The most common letters are: $x, y, z, a, b, c, m, and\ n$.<br>✓ Algebraic expression is an expression contains integers, variables, and the math operations such as addition, subtraction, multiplication, division, etc.<br>✓ In an expression, we can combine "like" terms. (values with same variable and same power) |
| **Example** | **Simplify this expression**. $(6x + 8x + 9) =?$<br><br>Combine like terms. Then: $(6x + 8x + 4) = 14x + 9$<br>**(remember you cannot combine variables and numbers).** |

| | | |
|---|---|---|
| **Your Turn!** | 1) $5x + 2 - 2x =$<br>$\qquad 3x + 2$ | 2) $4 + 7x + 3x =$<br>$\qquad 10x + 4$ |
| | 3) $8x + 3 - 3x =$<br>$\qquad 5x + 3$ | 4) $-2 - x^2 - 6x^2 =$<br>$\qquad -7x^2 - 2$ |
| | 5) $3 + 10x^2 + 2 =$<br>$\qquad 10x^2 + 5$ | 6) $8x^2 + 6x + 7x^2 =$<br>$\qquad 15x^2 + 6x$ |
| | 7) $5x^2 - 12x^2 + 8x =$<br>$\qquad -7x^2 + 8x$ | 8) $2x^2 - 2x - x + 5x^2 =$<br>$\qquad 72x^2 - 3x$ |
| | 9) $4x - (12 - 30x) =$<br>$\qquad 34x - 12$ | 10) $10x - (80x - 48) =$<br>$\qquad -70x - 48$ |

| Name: .............................. | Date: ................................... |
|---|---|

| **Topic** | **Simplifying Polynomial Expressions** |
|---|---|
| **Notes** | ✓ In mathematics, a polynomial is an expression consisting of variables and coefficients that involves only the operations of addition, subtraction, multiplication, and non–negative integer exponents of variables<br><br>$$P(x) = a_n x^n + a_{n-1} x^{n-1} + \ldots + a_2 x^2 + a_1 x + a_0$$ |
| **Example** | *Simplify this expression.* $(2x^2 - x^4) - (4x^4 - x^2) =$<br><br>First use distributive property:  → multiply $(-)$ into $(4x^4 - x^2)$<br><br>$(2x^2 - x^4) - (4x^4 - x^2) = 2x^2 - x^4 - 4x^4 + x^2$<br><br>Then combine "like" terms: $2x^2 - x^4 - 4x^4 + x^2 = 3x^2 - 5x^4$<br><br>And write in standard form: $3x^2 - 5x^4 = -5x^4 + 3x^2$ |

| **Your Turn!** | 1) $(2x^3 + 5x^2) - (12x + 2x^2) =$ | 2) $(2x^5 + 2x^3) - (7x^3 + 6x^2) =$ |
|---|---|---|
| | 3) $(12x^4 + 4x^2) - (2x^2 - 6x^4) =$ | 4) $14x - 3x^2 - 2(6x^2 + 6x^3) =$ |
| | 5) $(5x^3 - 3) + 5(2x^2 - 3x^3) =$ | 6) $(4x^3 - 2x) - 2(4x^3 - 2x^4) =$ |
| | 7) $2(4x - 3x^3) - 3(3x^3 + 4x^2) =$ | 8) $(2x^2 - 2x) - (2x^3 + 5x^2) =$ |

| Name: .................................... | Date: .................................... |
|---|---|

| Topic | **Simplifying Polynomial Expressions - Answers** |
|---|---|
| **Notes** | ✓ In mathematics, a polynomial is an expression consisting of variables and coefficients that involves only the operations of addition, subtraction, multiplication, and non–negative integer exponents of variables. $$P(x) = a_n x^n + a_{n-1} x^{n-1} + \ ... \ + \ a_2 x^2 \ + a_1 x + a_0$$ |
| **Example** | ***Simplify this expression.*** $(2x^2 - x^4) - (4x^4 - x^2) =$ <br><br> First use distributive property: $\rightarrow$ multiply $(-)$ into $(4x^4 - x^2)$ <br><br> $(2x^2 - x^4) - (4x^4 - x^2) = 2x^2 - x^4 - 4x^4 + x^2$ <br><br> Then combine "like" terms: $2x^2 - x^4 - 4x^4 + x^2 = 3x^2 - 5x^4$ <br><br> And write in standard form: $3x^2 - 5x^4 = -5x^4 + 3x^2$ |

| | | |
|---|---|---|
| **Your Turn!** | 1) $(2x^3 + 5x^2) - (12x + 2x^2) =$ <br><br> $2x^3 + 3x^2 - 12x$ | 2) $(2x^5 + 2x^3) - (7x^3 + 6x^2) =$ <br><br> $2x^5 - 5x^3 - 6x^2$ |
| | 3) $(12x^4 + 4x^2) - (2x^2 - 6x^4) =$ <br><br> $18x^4 + 2x^2$ | 4) $14x - 3x^2 - 2(6x^2 + 6x^3) =$ <br><br> $-12x^3 - 15x^2 + 14x$ |
| | 5) $(5x^3 - 3) + 5(2x^2 - 3x^3) =$ <br><br> $-10x^3 + 10x^2 - 3$ | 6) $(4x^3 - 2x) - 2(4x^3 - 2x^4) =$ <br><br> $4x^4 - 4x^3 - 2$ |
| | 7) $2(4x - 3x^3) - 3(3x^3 + 4x^2) =$ <br><br> $-15x^3 - 12x^2 + 8x$ | 8) $(2x^2 - 2x) - (2x^3 + 5x^2) =$ <br><br> $-2x^3 - 3x^2 - 2x$ |

| Name: ............................................ | Date: ................................................. |
|---|---|

| **Topic** | **Evaluating One Variable** |
|---|---|
| **Notes** | ✓ To evaluate one variable expression, find the variable and substitute a number for that variable. <br> ✓ Perform the arithmetic operations. |
| **Example** | *Find the value of this expression for* $x = -3.$ $-3x - 13$ <br><br> **Solution:** Substitute $-3$ for $x$, then: <br><br> $-3x - 13 = -3(-3) - 13 = 9 - 13 = -4$ |

| **Your Turn!** | 1) $x = -3 \Rightarrow 3x + 8 =$ _____ | 2) $x = 4 \Rightarrow 4(2x + 6) =$ _____ |
|---|---|---|
| | 3) $x = -1 \Rightarrow 6x + 4 =$ _____ | 4) $x = 7 \Rightarrow 6(5x + 3) =$ _____ |
| | 5) $x = 4 \Rightarrow 5(3x + 2) =$ ___ | 6) $x = 6 \Rightarrow 3(2x + 4) =$ _____ |
| | 7) $x = 3 \Rightarrow 7(3x + 1) =$ ___ | 8) $x = 8 \Rightarrow 3(3x + 7) =$ _____ |
| | 9) $x = 9 \Rightarrow 2(x + 9) =$ _____ | 10) $x = 7 \Rightarrow 2(4x + 5) =$ _____ |

| Name: .............................................. | Date: .................................................... |
|---|---|

| **Topic** | **Evaluating One Variable - Answers** |
|---|---|
| **Notes** | ✓ To evaluate one variable expression, find the variable and substitute a number for that variable.<br>✓ Perform the arithmetic operations |
| **Example** | *Find the value of this expression for* $x = -3$. $-3x - 13$<br><br>**Solution:** Substitute $-3$ for $x$, then:<br><br>$-3x - 13 = -3(-3) - 13 = 9 - 13 = -4$ |

| **Your Turn!** | | |
|---|---|---|
| | 1) $x = -3 \Rightarrow 3x + 8 = -1$ | 2) $x = 4 \Rightarrow 4(2x + 6) = 56$ |
| | 3) $x = -1 \Rightarrow 6x + 4 = -2$ | 4) $x = 7 \Rightarrow 6(5x + 3) = 228$ |
| | 5) $x = 4 \Rightarrow 5(3x + 2) = 70$ | 6) $x = 6 \Rightarrow 3(2x + 4) = 48$ |
| | 7) $x = 3 \Rightarrow 7(3x + 1) = 70$ | 8) $x = 8 \Rightarrow 3(3x + 7) = 93$ |
| | 9) $x = 9 \Rightarrow 2(x + 9) = 36$ | 10) $x = 7 \Rightarrow 2(4x + 5) = 66$ |

| Name: .............................. | Date: ...................................... |
|---|---|

| Topic | **Evaluating Two Variables** |
|---|---|
| **Notes** | ✓ To evaluate an algebraic expression, substitute a number for each variable. <br> ✓ Perform the arithmetic operations to find the value of the expression. |
| **Example** | *Evaluate this expression for* $a = 4$ *and* $b = -2$.   $5a - 6b$ <br><br> **Solution:** Substitute 4 for $a$, and $-2$ for $b$, then: <br><br> $5a - 6b = 5(4) - 6(-2) = 20 + 12 = 32$ |

| | | |
|---|---|---|
| **Your Turn!** | 1) $-4a + 6b, \ a = 4, \ b = 3$ <br><br> _____ | 2) $5x + 3y, \ x = 2, \ y = -1$ <br><br> _____ |
| | 3) $-5a + 3b, \ a = 2, \ b = -2$ <br><br> _____ | 4) $3x - 4y, \ x = 6, \ y = 2$ <br><br> _____ |
| | 5) $2z + 14 + 6k, \ z = 5,$ <br> $k = 3$ <br><br> _____ | 6) $7a - (9 - 3b), \ a = 1,$ <br> $b = 1$ <br><br> _____ |
| | 7) $-6a + 3b, \ a = 4, \ b = 3$ <br><br> _____ | 8) $-2a + b, \ a = 6, \ b = 9$ <br><br> _____ |
| | 9) $8x + 2y, \ x = 4, \ y = 5$ <br><br> _____ | 10) $z + 4 + 2k, \ z = 7, \ k = 4$ <br><br> _____ |

| Name: .................................................... | Date: ........................................................ |
|---|---|
| **Topic** | **Evaluating Two Variables - Answers** |
| **Notes** | ✓ To evaluate an algebraic expression, substitute a number for each variable.<br>✓ Perform the arithmetic operations to find the value of the expression. |
| **Example** | ***Evaluate this expression for*** $a = 4$ ***and*** $b = -2$. $\;\; 5a - 6b$<br><br>**Solution:** Substitute 4 for $a$, and $-2$ for $b$, then:<br><br>$\quad 5a - 6b = \; 5(4) - 6(-2) = 20 + 12 = 32$ |

| | | |
|---|---|---|
| **Your Turn!** | 1) $-4a + 6b, \; a = 4, \; b = 3$<br><br>2 | 2) $5x + 3y, \; x = 2, \; y = -1$<br><br>7 |
| | 3) $-5a + 3b, \; a = 2, \; b = -2$<br>$-16$ | 4) $3x - 4y, \; x = 6, \; y = 2$<br>10 |
| | 5) $2z + 14 + 6k, \; z = 5,$<br>$\qquad\qquad k = 3$<br><br>42 | 6) $7a - (9 - 3b), \; a = 1,$<br>$\qquad\qquad b = 1$<br><br>1 |
| | 7) $-6a + 3b, \; a = 4, \; b = 3$<br>$-15$ | 8) $-2a + b, \; a = 6, \; b = 9$<br>$-3$ |
| | 9) $8x + 2y, \; x = 4, \; y = 5$<br>42 | 10) $z + 4 + 2k, \; z = 7, \; k = 4$<br>19 |

| Name: .............................................. | Date: .......................................................... |
|---|---|

| Topic | **The Distributive Property** |
|---|---|
| **Notes** | ✓ The distributive property (or the distributive property of multiplication over addition and subtraction) simplifies and solves expressions in the form of: $a(b + c)$ or $a(b - c)$ <br> ✓ Distributive Property rule: <br> $$a(b + c) = ab + ac$$ |
| **Example** | ***Simply.*** $(5)(2x - 8)$ <br><br> **Solution:** Use Distributive Property rule: $a(b + c) = ab + ac$ <br><br> $$(5)(2x - 8) = (5 \times 2x) + (5) \times (-8) = 10x - 40$$ |

| **Your Turn!** | | |
|---|---|---|
| | 1) $(-2)(4 - 3x) =$ | 2) $(6 - 3x)(-7)$ |
| | 3) $6\,(5 - 9x) =$ | 4) $10(3 - 5x) =$ |
| | 5) $5(6 - 5x) =$ | 6) $(-2)(-5x + 3) =$ |
| | 7) $(8 - 9x)(5) =$ | 8) $(-16x + 15)(-3) =$ |
| | 9) $(-2x + 7)(3) =$ | 10) $(-18x + 25)(-2) =$ |

| Name: ............................................ | Date: ............................................ |
|---|---|

| Topic | **The Distributive Property - Answers** | |
|---|---|---|
| **Notes** | ✓ The distributive property (or the distributive property of multiplication over addition and subtraction) simplifies and solves expressions in the form of: $a(b + c)$ or $a(b - c)$ <br> ✓ Distributive Property rule: <br> $$a(b + c) = ab + ac$$ | |
| **Example** | **Simply.** $(5)(2x - 8)$ <br><br> **Solution:** Use Distributive Property rule: $a(b + c) = ab + ac$ <br><br> $$(5)(2x - 8) = (5 \times 2x) + (5) \times (-8) = 10x - 40$$ | |
| **Your Turn!** | 1) $(-2)(4 - 3x) = 6x - 8$ | 2) $(6 - 3x)(-7) = 21x - 42$ |
| | 3) $6(5 - 9x) = -54x + 30$ | 4) $10(3 - 5x) = -50x + 30$ |
| | 5) $5(6 - 5x) = -25x + 30$ | 6) $(-2)(-5x + 3) = 10x - 6$ |
| | 7) $(8 - 9x)(5) = -45x + 40$ | 8) $(-16x + 15)(-3) =$ <br><br> $48x - 45$ |
| | 9) $(-2x + 7)(3) = -6x + 21$ | 10)$(-18x + 25)(-2) =$ <br><br> $36x - 50$ |

| Name: ............................................... | Date: ............................................................. |
|---|---|

| **Topic** | **One–Step Equations** |
|---|---|
| **Notes** | ✓  You only need to perform one Math operation in order to solve the one-step equations. <br> ✓  To solve one-step equation, find the inverse (opposite) operation is being performed. <br> ✓  The inverse operations are: <br>   -  Addition and subtraction <br>   -  Multiplication and division |
| **Example** | *Solve this equation*.  $x + 42 = 60 \Rightarrow x = ?$ <br>   Here, the operation is addition and its inverse operation is subtraction. To solve this equation, subtract 42 from both sides of the *equation:* <br> $x + 42 - 42 = 60 - 42$ <br> Then simplify: $x + 42 - 42 = 60 - 42 \Rightarrow x = 18$ |

| **Your Turn!** | 1) $x - 15 = 36 \Rightarrow x = $ ____ | 2) $18 = 13 + x \Rightarrow x = $ ____ |
|---|---|---|
| | 3) $x - 22 = 54 \Rightarrow x = $ ____ | 4) $x + 14 = 24 \Rightarrow x = $ ____ |
| | 5) $4x = 24 \Rightarrow x = $ ____ | 6) $\frac{x}{6} = -3 \Rightarrow x = $ ____ |
| | 7) $99 = 11x \Rightarrow x = $ ____ | 8) $\frac{x}{12} = 6 \Rightarrow x = $ ____ |

| Name: .................................. | | Date: .................................. |
|---|---|---|

| Topic | One–Step Equations - Answers | |
|---|---|---|
| **Notes** | ✓ You only need to perform one Math operation in order to solve the one-step equations.<br>✓ To solve one-step equation, find the inverse (opposite) operation is being performed.<br>✓ The inverse operations are:<br>  - Addition and subtraction<br>  - Multiplication and division | |
| **Example** | ***Solve this equation.*** $x + 42 = 60 \Rightarrow x = ?$<br>Here, the operation is addition and its inverse operation is subtraction. To solve this equation, subtract 42 from both sides of the *equation*:<br>$x + 42 - 42 = 60 - 42$<br>Then simplify: $x + 42 - 42 = 60 - 42 \Rightarrow x = 18$ | |
| **Your Turn!** | 1) $x - 15 = 36 \Rightarrow x = 51$ | 2) $18 = 13 + x \Rightarrow x = 5$ |
| | 3) $x - 22 = 54 \Rightarrow x = 76$ | 4) $x + 14 = 24 \Rightarrow x = 10$ |
| | 5) $4x = 24 \Rightarrow x = 6$ | 6) $\frac{x}{6} = -3 \Rightarrow x = -18$ |
| | 7) $99 = 11x \Rightarrow x = 9$ | 8) $\frac{x}{12} = 6 \Rightarrow x = 72$ |

| Name: .................................................... | Date: .................................................... |

| Topic | Multi –Step Equations |
|---|---|
| **Notes** | ✓ Combine "like" terms on one side. <br> ✓ Bring variables to one side by adding or subtracting. <br> ✓ Simplify using the inverse of addition or subtraction. <br> ✓ Simplify further by using the inverse of multiplication or division. <br> ✓ Check your solution by plugging the value of the variable into the original equation. |
| **Example** | **Solve this equation for** $x$. $\quad 2x - 3 = 13$ <br><br> **Solution:** The inverse of subtraction is addition. Add 3 to both sides of the equation. <br><br> Then: $2x - 3 = 13 \Rightarrow 2x - 3 = 13 + 3$ <br><br> $\Rightarrow 2x = 16$. Now, divide both sides by 2, then: $\frac{2x}{2} = \frac{16}{2} \Rightarrow x = 8$ <br><br> Now, check the solution: $x = 8 \Rightarrow 2x - 3 = 13 \Rightarrow 2(8) - 3 = 13 \Rightarrow 16 - 3 = 13 \qquad$ The answer $x = 8$ is correct. |

| **Your Turn!** | 1) $4x - 12 = 8 \Rightarrow x =$ | 2) $12 - 3x = -6 + 3x \Rightarrow x =$ |
|---|---|---|
| | 3) $3(4 - 2x) = 24 \Rightarrow x =$ | 4) $15 + 5x = -7 - 6x \Rightarrow x =$ |
| | 5) $-2(5 + x) = 2 \Rightarrow x =$ | 6) $12 - 2x = -3 - 5x \Rightarrow x =$ |
| | 7) $14 = -(x - 9) \Rightarrow x =$ | 8) $11 - 4x = -4 - 3x \Rightarrow x =$ |

| Name: ......................................................... | Date: ......................................................... |
|---|---|

| Topic | **Multi –Step Equations - Answers** |
|---|---|
| **Notes** | ✓ Combine "like" terms on one side.<br>✓ Bring variables to one side by adding or subtracting.<br>✓ Simplify using the inverse of addition or subtraction.<br>✓ Simplify further by using the inverse of multiplication or division.<br>✓ Check your solution by plugging the value of the variable into the original equation. |
| **Example** | ***Solve this equation for*** $x$. $\quad 2x - 3 = 13$<br><br>**Solution:** The inverse of subtraction is addition. Add 3 to both sides of the equation.<br><br>Then: $2x - 3 = 13 \Rightarrow 2x - 3 = 13 + 3$<br><br>$\Rightarrow 2x = 16$. Now, divide both sides by 2, then: $\frac{2x}{2} = \frac{16}{2} \Rightarrow x = 8$<br><br>Now, check the solution: $x = 8 \Rightarrow 2x - 3 = 13 \Rightarrow 2(8) - 3 = 13 \Rightarrow 16 - 3 = 13$ $\qquad$ The answer $x = 8$ is correct. |
| **Your Turn!** | 1) $4x - 12 = 8 \Rightarrow x = 5$ $\qquad$ 2) $12 - 3x = -6 + 3x \Rightarrow x = 3$<br><br>3) $3(4 - 2x) = 24 \Rightarrow x = -2$ $\qquad$ 4) $15 + 5x = -7 - 6x \Rightarrow x = -2$<br><br>5) $-2(5 + x) = 2 \Rightarrow x = -6$ $\qquad$ 6) $12 - 2x = -3 - 5x \Rightarrow x = -5$<br><br>7) $14 = -(x - 9) \Rightarrow x = -5$ $\qquad$ 8) $11 - 4x = -4 - 3x \Rightarrow x = 15$ |

| Name: ................................ | Date: .......................................... |
|---|---|

| Topic | **System of Equations** |
|---|---|
| **Notes** | ✓ A system of equations contains two equations and two variables. For example, consider the system of equations: $x - 2y = -2, x + 2y = 10$<br>✓ The easiest way to solve a system of equation is using the elimination method. The elimination method uses the addition property of equality. You can add the same value to each side of an equation.<br>✓ For the first equation above, you can add $x + 2y$ to the left side and 10 to the right side of the first equation: $x - 2y + (x + 2y) = -2 + 10$. Now, if you simplify, you get: $x - 2y + (x + 2y) = -2 + 10 \rightarrow 2x = 8 \rightarrow x = 4$. Now, substitute 4 for the $x$ in the first equation: $4 - 2y = -2$. By solving this equation, $y = 3$ |
| **Example** | What is the value of $x$ and $y$ in this system of equations? $\begin{cases} 3x - y = 7 \\ -x + 4y = 5 \end{cases}$<br><br>**Solution:** Solving System of Equations by Elimination: $\begin{array}{l} 3x - y = 7 \\ \underline{-x + 4y = 5} \end{array}$<br><br>Multiply the second equation by 3, then add it to the first equation.<br>$\begin{array}{l} 3x - y = 7 \\ 3(-x + 4y = 5) \end{array} \Rightarrow \begin{array}{l} 3x - y = 7 \\ -3x + 12y = 15 \end{array} \Rightarrow 11y = 22 \Rightarrow y = 2$. Now, substitute 2 for $y$ in the first equation and solve for $x$.<br>$3x - (2) = 7 \Rightarrow 3x = 9 \Rightarrow x = 3$ |
| **Your Turn!** | 1) $-4x + 4y = 8$<br>$-4x + 2y = 6$<br>$x = \_\_\_$<br>$y = \_\_\_$ <br><br> 2) $-5x + y = -3$<br>$3x - 8y = 24$<br>$x = \_\_\_$<br>$y = \_\_\_$ <br><br> 3) $y = -2$<br>$4x - 3y = 8$<br>$x = \_\_\_$<br>$y = \_\_\_$ <br><br> 4) $y = -3x + 5$<br>$5x - 4y = -3$<br>$x = \_\_\_$<br>$y = \_\_\_$ <br><br> 5) $20x - 18y = -26$<br>$-10x + 6y = 22$<br>$x = \_\_\_$<br>$y = \_\_\_$ <br><br> 6) $-9x - 12y = 15$<br>$2x - 6y = 14$<br>$x = \_\_\_$<br>$y = \_\_\_$ |

| Name: ..................................... | Date: ..................................... |
|---|---|

| Topic | **System of Equations- Answers** |
|---|---|
| **Notes** | ✓ A system of equations contains two equations and two variables. For example, consider the system of equations: $x - 2y = -2, x + 2y = 10$<br>✓ The easiest way to solve a system of equation is using the elimination method. The elimination method uses the addition property of equality. You can add the same value to each side of an equation.<br>✓ For the first equation above, you can add $x + 2y$ to the left side and 10 to the right side of the first equation: $x - 2y + (x + 2y) = -2 + 10$. Now, if you simplify, you get: $x - 2y + (x + 2y) = -2 + 10 \rightarrow 2x = 8 \rightarrow x = 4$. Now, substitute 4 for the $x$ in the first equation: $4 - 2y = -2$. By solving this equation, $y = 3$ |
| **Example** | What is the value of $x$ and $y$ in this system of equations? $\begin{cases} 3x - y = 7 \\ -x + 4y = 5 \end{cases}$<br><br>**Solution:** Solving System of Equations by Elimination: $\begin{array}{l} 3x - y = 7 \\ -x + 4y = 5 \end{array}$<br><br>Multiply the second equation by 3, then add it to the first equation.<br><br>$\begin{array}{l} 3x - y = 7 \\ 3(-x + 4y = 5) \end{array} \Rightarrow \begin{array}{l} 3x - y = 7 \\ -3x + 12y = 15) \end{array} \Rightarrow 11y = 22 \Rightarrow y = 2$. Now, substitute 2 for $y$ in the first equation and solve for $x$.<br><br>$3x - (2) = 7 \Rightarrow 3x = 9 \Rightarrow x = 3$ |
| **Your Turn!** | 1) $-4x + 4y = 8$<br>$-4x + 2y = 6$ |

| **Your Turn!** | 1) $-4x + 4y = 8$ <br> $-4x + 2y = 6$ | 2) $-5x + y = -3$ <br> $3x - 8y = 24$ |
|---|---|---|
| | $x = -1$ <br>   $\quad y = 1$ | $x = 0$ <br>   $\quad y = -3$ |
| | 3) $y = -2$ <br> $4x - 3y = 8$ | 4) $y = -3x + 5$ <br> $5x - 4y = -3$ |
| | $x = \dfrac{1}{2}$ <br>   $\quad y = -2$ | $x = 1$ <br>   $\quad y = 2$ |
| | 5) $20x - 18y = -26$ <br> $10x + 6y = 22$ | 6) $-9x - 12y = 15$ <br> $2x \quad 6y - 14$ |
| | $x = -4$ <br>   $\quad y = -3$ | $x = 1$ <br>   $\quad y = -2$ |

| Name: .................................. | Date: ............................................... |
|---|---|

| **Topic** | **Graphing Single–Variable Inequalities** |
|---|---|
| **Notes** | ✓ An inequality compares two expressions using an inequality sign.<br>✓ Inequality signs are: "less than" <, "greater than" >, "less than or equal to" ≤, and "greater than or equal to" ≥.<br>✓ To graph a single–variable inequality, find the value of the inequality on the number line.<br>✓ For less than (<) or greater than (>) draw open circle on the value of the variable. If there is an equal sign too, then use filled circle.<br>✓ Draw an arrow to the right for greater or to the left for less than. |
| **Example** | ***Draw a graph for this inequality.*** $x < 5$<br>**Solution:** Since, the variable is less than 5, then we need to find 5 in the number line and draw an open circle on it. Then, draw an arrow to the left.<br><br>-6 -5 -4 -3 -2 -1 0 1 2 3 4 5 6 |
| **Your Turn!** | 1) $x < 4$  <br>2) $x \geq -1$  <br>3) $x \geq -3$  <br>4) $x \leq 6$  <br>5) $x > -6$  <br>6) $2 > x$  <br>7) $-2 \leq x$  <br>8) $x > 0$ |

| Name: .................................. | Date: ............................................. |
|---|---|

| Topic | **Graphing Single–Variable Inequalities- Answers** |
|---|---|
| **Notes** | ✓ An inequality compares two expressions using an inequality sign.<br>✓ Inequality signs are: "less than" <, "greater than" >, "less than or equal to" ≤, and "greater than or equal to" ≥.<br>✓ To graph a single–variable inequality, find the value of the inequality on the number line.<br>✓ For less than (<) or greater than (>) draw open circle on the value of the variable. If there is an equal sign too, then use filled circle.<br>✓ Draw an arrow to the right for greater or to the left for less than. |
| **Example** | ***Draw a graph for this inequality.*** $x < 5$<br>**Solution:** Since, the variable is less than 5, then we need to find 5 in the number line and draw an open circle on it. Then, draw an arrow to the left. |

**Your Turn!**

1) $x < 4$

2) $x \geq -1$

3) $x \geq -3$

4) $x \leq 6$

5) $x > -6$

6) $2 > x$

7) $-2 \leq x$

8) $x > 0$

| **Name:** ............................................. | **Date:** ................................................. |
|---|---|

| | | |
|---|---|---|
| **Topic** | **One–Step Inequalities** | |
| **Notes** | ✓ Inequality signs are: "less than" $<$, "greater than" $>$, "less than or equal to" $\leq$, and "greater than or equal to" $\geq$.<br>✓ You only need to perform one Math operation in order to solve the one step inequalities.<br>✓ To solve one-step inequalities, find the inverse (opposite) operation is being performed.<br>✓ For dividing or multiplying both sides by negative numbers, flip the direction of the inequality sign. | |
| **Example** | ***Solve this inequality.*** $x + 12 < 60 \Rightarrow$ ______<br>Here, the operation is addition and its inverse operation is subtraction. To solve this inequality, subtract 12 from both sides of the ***inequality:*** $x + 12 - 12 < 60 - 12$<br>Then simplify: $x < 48$ | |
| **Your Turn!** | 1) $4x < -8 \Rightarrow$ ______ | 2) $x + 6 > 28 \Rightarrow$ ______ |
| | 3) $-3x \geq 36 \Rightarrow$ ______ | 4) $x - 16 \leq 4 \Rightarrow$ ______ |
| | 5) $\frac{x}{2} \geq -9 \Rightarrow$ ______ | 6) $48 < 6x \Rightarrow$ ______ |
| | 7) $77 \leq 11x \Rightarrow$ ______ | 8) $\frac{x}{4} > 9 \Rightarrow$ ______ |

| Name: ................................................ | Date: ...................................................... |
|---|---|

| Topic | One–Step Inequalities - Answers |
|---|---|
| **Notes** | ✓ Inequality signs are: "less than" <, "greater than" >, "less than or equal to" ≤, and "greater than or equal to" ≥.<br>✓ You only need to perform one Math operation in order to solve the one-step inequalities.<br>✓ To solve one-step inequalities, find the inverse (opposite) operation is being performed.<br>✓ For dividing or multiplying both sides by negative numbers, flip the direction of the inequality sign. |
| **Example** | ***Solve this inequality.***  $x + 12 < 60 \Rightarrow$ _____<br>Here, the operation is addition and its inverse operation is subtraction. To solve this inequality, subtract 12 from both sides of the ***inequality:*** $x + 12 - 12 < 60 - 12$<br>Then simplify: $x < 48$ |

| **Your Turn!** | | |
|---|---|---|
| | 1) $4x < -8 \Rightarrow x < -2$ | 2) $x + 6 > 28 \Rightarrow x > 22$ |
| | 3) $-3x \geq 36 \Rightarrow x \leq -12$ | 4) $x - 16 \leq 4 \Rightarrow x \leq 20$ |
| | 5) $\frac{x}{2} \geq -9 \Rightarrow x \geq -18$ | 6) $48 < 6x \Rightarrow 8 < x$ |
| | 7) $77 \leq 11x \Rightarrow 7 \leq x$ | 8) $\frac{x}{4} > 9 \Rightarrow x > 36$ |

| Name: .......................................... | Date: .............................................. |
|---|---|

| **Topic** | **Multi –Step Inequalities** |
|---|---|
| **Notes** | ✓ Isolate the variable.<br>✓ Simplify using the inverse of addition or subtraction.<br>✓ Simplify further by using the inverse of multiplication or division.<br>✓ For dividing or multiplying both sides by negative numbers, flip the direction of the inequality sign. |
| **Example** | ***Solve this inequality.*** $3x + 12 \leq 21$<br>**Solution:** First subtract 12 from both sides: $3x + 12 - 12 \leq 21 - 12$<br>Then simplify: $3x + 12 - 12 \leq 21 - 12 \rightarrow 3x \leq 9$<br>Now divide both sides by 3: $\frac{3x}{3} \leq \frac{9}{3} \rightarrow x \leq 3$ |
| **Your Turn!** | 1) $5x + 6 < 36 \rightarrow$ _____    2) $2x - 8 \leq 6 \rightarrow$ _____<br><br>3) $2x - 5 \leq 17 \rightarrow$ _____    4) $14 - 7x \geq -7 \rightarrow$ _____<br><br>5) $18 - 6x \geq -6 \rightarrow$ _____    6) $2x - 18 \leq 16 \rightarrow$ _____<br><br>7) $8 + 4x < 44 \rightarrow$ _____    8) $5 - 4x < 17 \rightarrow$ _____ |

| Name: .............................. | Date: ..................................... |
|---|---|

| Topic | **Multi –Step Inequalities - Answers** |
|---|---|
| **Notes** | ✓ Isolate the variable.<br>✓ Simplify using the inverse of addition or subtraction.<br>✓ Simplify further by using the inverse of multiplication or division.<br>✓ For dividing or multiplying both sides by negative numbers, flip the direction of the inequality sign. |
| **Example** | **Solve this inequality.** $3x + 12 \leq 21$<br>**Solution:** First subtract 12 from both sides: $3x + 12 - 12 \leq 21 - 12$<br>Then simplify: $3x + 12 - 12 \leq 21 - 12 \rightarrow 3x \leq 9$<br>Now divide both sides by 3: $\frac{3x}{3} \leq \frac{9}{3} \rightarrow x \leq 3$ |

| **Your Turn!** | 1) $5x + 6 < 36 \rightarrow x < 6$ | 2) $2x - 8 \leq 6 \rightarrow x \leq 7$ |
|---|---|---|
| | 3) $2x - 5 \leq 17 \rightarrow x \leq 11$ | 4) $14 - 7x \geq -7 \rightarrow x \leq 3$ |
| | 5) $18 - 6x \geq -6 \rightarrow x \leq 4$ | 6) $2x - 18 \leq 16 \rightarrow x \leq 17$ |
| | 7) $8 + 4x < 44 \rightarrow x < 9$ | 8) $5 - 4x < 17 \rightarrow x > -3$ |

| Name: ............................................... | Date: ............................................... |

| **Topic** | **Finding Slope** |
|---|---|
| **Notes** | ✓ The slope of a line represents the direction of a line on the coordinate plane.<br>✓ A line on coordinate plane can be drawn by connecting two points.<br>✓ To find the slope of a line, we need two points.<br>✓ The slope of a line with two points A $(x_1, y_1)$ and B $(x_2, y_2)$ can be found by using this formula: $\frac{y_2 - y_1}{x_2 - x_1} = \frac{rise}{run}$<br>✓ The equation of a line is typically written as $y = mx + b$ where $m$ is the slope and $b$ is the $y$-intercept. |
| **Examples** | ***Find the slope of the line through these two points:*** $(4, -12)$ *and* $(9, 8)$.<br><br>**Solution:** Slope $= \frac{y_2 - y_1}{x_2 - x_1}$. Let $(x_1, y_1)$ be $(4, -12)$ and $(x_2, y_2)$ be $(9, 8)$.<br>***Then:*** slope $= \frac{y_2 - y_1}{x_2 - x_1} = \frac{8 - (-12)}{9 - 4} = \frac{8 + 12}{5} = \frac{20}{5} = 4$<br>***Find the slope of the line with equation*** $y = 5x - 6$<br>**Solution:** when the equation of a line is written in the form of $y = mx + b$, the slope is $m$. In this line: $y = 5x - 6$, the slope is 5. |
| **Your Turn!** | 1) $(2, 3), (4, 7)$<br><br>Slope = ____      2) $(-2, 2), (0, 4)$<br><br>Slope = ____<br><br>3) $(4, -2), (2, 4)$<br><br>Slope = ____      4) $(-4, -1), (0, 7)$<br><br>Slope = ____<br><br>5) $y = 3x + 18$<br><br>Slope = ____      6) $y = 12x - 3$<br><br>Slope = ____ |

| Name: .............................................. | Date: ................................................. |

| Topic | **Finding Slope - Answers** |
|---|---|
| **Notes** | ✓ The slope of a line represents the direction of a line on the coordinate plane.<br>✓ A line on coordinate plane can be drawn by connecting two points.<br>✓ To find the slope of a line, we need two points.<br>✓ The slope of a line with two points A $(x_1, y_1)$ and B $(x_2, y_2)$ can be found by using this formula: $\frac{y_2 - y_1}{x_2 - x_1} = \frac{rise}{run}$<br>✓ The equation of a line is typically written as $y = mx + b$ where $m$ is the slope and $b$ is the $y$-intercept. |
| **Examples** | ***Find the slope of the line through these two points:*** $(4, -12)$ *and* $(9, 8)$.<br>**Solution:** Slope $= \frac{y_2 - y_1}{x_2 - x_1}$. Let $(x_1, y_1)$ be $(4, -12)$ and $(x_2, y_2)$ be $(9, 8)$.<br>***Then:*** slope $= \frac{y_2 - y_1}{x_2 - x_1} = \frac{8 - (-12)}{9 - 4} = \frac{8 + 12}{5} = \frac{20}{5} = 4$<br>***Find the slope of the line with equation*** $y = 5x - 6$<br>**Solution:** when the equation of a line is written in the form of $y = mx + b$, the slope is $m$. In this line: $y = 5x - 6$, the slope is 5. |

| | | |
|---|---|---|
| **Your Turn!** | 1) $(2, 3), (4, 7)$<br><br>Slope $= 2$ | 2) $(-2, 2), (0, 4)$<br><br>Slope $= 1$ |
| | 3) $(4, -2), (2, 4)$<br><br>Slope $= -3$ | 4) $(-4, -1), (0, 7)$<br><br>Slope $= 2$ |
| | 5) $y = 3x + 18$<br><br>Slope $= 3$ | 6) $y = 12x - 3$<br><br>Slope $= 12$ |

| Name: ................................ | Date: ................................ |
|---|---|

| **Topic** | **Graphing Lines Using Slope–Intercept Form** |
|---|---|
| **Notes** | ✓ Slope–intercept form of a line: given the slope **m** and the **y**–intercept (the intersection of the line and y-axis) **b**, then the equation of the line is:<br>$$y = mx + b$$ |

| **Example** | **Sketch the graph of** $y = -2\text{x} - 1$.<br>**Solution:** To graph this line, we need to find two points. When $x$ is zero the value of $y$ is $-1$. And when $y$ is zero the value of x is $-\frac{1}{2}$.<br><br>$$x = 0 \rightarrow y = -2(0) - 1 = -1, y = 0 \rightarrow 0$$<br>$$= -2x - 1 \rightarrow x = -\frac{1}{2}$$<br><br>Now, we have two points: $(0, -1)$ and $(-\frac{1}{2}, 0)$. Find the points and graph the line.<br><br>Remember that the slope of the line is $-\frac{1}{2}$. |
|---|---|

| **Your Turn!** | 1) $y = -4x + 1$ | 2) $y = -x - 5$ |
|---|---|---|

| Name: ................................... | Date: ................................... |
|---|---|

| **Topic** | **Graphing Lines Using Slope–Intercept Form - Answers** |
|---|---|
| **Notes** | ✓ Slope–intercept form of a line: given the slope $m$ and the $y$–intercept (the intersection of the line and y-axis) $b$, then the equation of the line is: $$y = mx + h$$ |
| **Example** | ***Sketch the graph of*** $y = -2x - 1$. <br><br> **Solution:** To graph this line, we need to find two points. When $x$ is zero the value of $y$ is $-1$. And when $y$ is zero the value of x is $-\frac{1}{2}$. <br><br> $$x = 0 \rightarrow y = -2(0) - 1 = -1, y = 0 \rightarrow 0$$ $$= -2x - 1 \rightarrow x = -\frac{1}{2}$$ <br> Now, we have two points: $(0, -1)$ and $(-\frac{1}{2}, 0)$. Find the points and graph the line. <br><br> Remember that the slope of the line is $-\frac{1}{2}$. |
| **Your Turn!** | 1) $y = -4x + 1$     2) $y = -x - 5$ |

| Name: .................................... | Date: ................................................. |
|---|---|

| Topic | Writing Linear Equations | |
|---|---|---|
| **Notes** | ✓ The equation of a line: $y = mx + b$ <br> ✓ Identify the slope. <br> ✓ Find the y-intercept. This can be done by substituting the slope and the coordinates of a point $(x, y)$ on the line. | |
| **Example** | **Write the equation of the line through $(3, 1)$ and $(-1, 5)$.** <br> **Solution:** $Slop = \frac{y_2 - y_1}{x_2 - x_1} = \frac{5 - 1}{-1 - 3} = \frac{4}{-4} = -1 \rightarrow m = -1$ <br> To find the value of $b$, you can use either points. <br> The answer will be the same: $y = -x + b$ <br> $(3, 1) \rightarrow 1 = -3 + b \rightarrow b = 4$ <br> $(-1, 5) \rightarrow 5 = -(-1) + b \rightarrow b = 4$ <br> The equation of the line is: $y = -x + 4$ | |
| **Your Turn!** | 1) through: $(-2, 7), (1, 4)$ <br><br> $y =$ | 2) through: $(6, 1), (5, 2)$ <br><br> $y =$ |
| | 3) through: $(5, -1), (8, 2)$ <br><br> $y =$ | 4) through: $(-2, 4), (4, -8)$ <br><br> $y =$ |
| | 5) through: $(6, -5), (-5, 6)$ <br><br> $y =$ | 6) through: $(4, -4), (-2, 8)$ <br><br> $y =$ |
| | 7) through $(8, 8)$, Slope: 2 <br><br> $y =$ | 8) through $(-7, 10)$, Slope: $-2$ <br><br> $y =$ |

| Name: …………………………… | Date: ………………………………… |
|---|---|

| Topic | **Writing Linear Equations - Answers** |
|---|---|
| **Notes** | ✓ The equation of a line: $y = mx + b$ <br> ✓ Identify the slope. <br> ✓ Find the y–intercept. This can be done by substituting the slope and the coordinates of a point $(x, y)$ on the line. |
| **Example** | **Write the equation of the line through $(3, 1)$ and $(-1, 5)$.** <br> **Solution:** $Slop = \frac{y_2 - y_1}{x_2 - x_1} = \frac{5 - 1}{-1 - 3} = \frac{4}{-4} = -1 \rightarrow m = -1$ <br> To find the value of $b$, you can use either points. <br> The answer will be the same: $y = -x + b$ <br> $(3, 1) \rightarrow 1 = -3 + b \rightarrow b = 4$ <br> $(-1, 5) \rightarrow 5 = -(-1) + b \rightarrow b = 4$ <br> The equation of the line is: $y = -x + 4$ |

| | | |
|---|---|---|
| **Your Turn!** | 1) through: $(-2, 7), (1, 4)$ <br><br> $y = -x + 5$ | 2) through: $(6, 1), (5, 2)$ <br><br> $y = -x + 7$ |
| | 3) through: $(5, -1), (8, 2)$ <br><br> $y = x - 6$ | 4) through: $(-2, 4), (4, -8)$ <br><br> $y = -2x$ |
| | 5) through: $(6, -5), (-5, 6)$ <br><br> $y = -x + 1$ | 6) through: $(4, -4), (-2, 8)$ <br><br> $y = -2x + 4$ |
| | 7) through $(8, 8)$, Slope: 2 <br><br> $y = 2x - 8$ | 8) through $(-7, 10)$, Slope: $-2$ <br><br> $y = -2x - 4$ |

| Name: ................................. | Date: ................................................ |

| Topic | **Finding Midpoint** |
|---|---|
| **Notes** | ✓ The middle of a line segment is its midpoint. <br><br> ✓ The Midpoint of two endpoints A $(x_1, y_1)$ and B $(x_2, y_2)$ can be found using this formula. $M(\frac{x_1+x_2}{2}, \frac{y_1+y_2}{2})$ |
| **Example** | Find the midpoint of the line segment with the given endpoints. $(\mathbf{1}, -\mathbf{2}), (\mathbf{3}, \mathbf{6})$ <br><br> **Solution:** Midpoint $= (\frac{x_1+x_2}{2}, \frac{y_1+y_2}{2}) \rightarrow (x_1, y_1) = (1, -2)$ and $(x_2, y_2) = (3, 6)$ <br> Midpoint $= (\frac{1+3}{2}, \frac{-2+6}{2}) \rightarrow (\frac{4}{2}, \frac{4}{2}) \rightarrow M(2, 2)$ |

| **Your Turn!** | 1) $(6, 0), (-4, 2)$ <br><br> **Midpoint** $= (\_\_, \_\_)$ | 2) $(4, -1), (2, 3)$ <br><br> **Midpoint** $= (\_\_, \_\_)$ |
|---|---|---|
| | 3) $(-3, 4), (-5, 0)$ <br><br> **Midpoint** $= (\_\_, \_\_)$ | 4) $(8, 1), (-4, 5)$ <br><br> **Midpoint** $= (\_\_, \_\_)$ |
| | 5) $(6, 7), (-4, 5)$ <br><br> **Midpoint** $= (\_\_, \_\_)$ | 6) $(2, -3), (2, 5)$ <br><br> **Midpoint** $= (\_\_, \_\_)$ |
| | 7) $(7, 3), (-1, -7)$ <br><br> **Midpoint** $= (\_\_, \_\_)$ | 8) $(3, 9), (-1, 5)$ <br><br> **Midpoint** $= (\_\_, \_\_)$ |
| | 9) $(3, 4), (-7, -6)$ <br><br> **Midpoint** $= (\_\_, \_\_)$ | 10) $(-5, 2), (11, -6)$ <br><br> **Midpoint** $= (\_\_, \_\_)$ |

| Name: ............................................ | Date: ..................................................... |
|---|---|

| Topic | **Finding Midpoint - Answers** |
|---|---|
| **Notes** | ✓ The middle of a line segment is its midpoint. <br><br> ✓ The Midpoint of two endpoints A $(x_1, y_1)$ and B $(x_2, y_2)$ can be found using this formula: $M(\frac{x_1+x_2}{2}, \frac{y_1+y_2}{2})$ |
| **Example** | Find the midpoint of the line segment with the given endpoints. $(\mathbf{1}, -\mathbf{2}), (\mathbf{3}, \mathbf{6})$ <br><br> **Solution:** Midpoint $= (\frac{x_1+x_2}{2}, \frac{y_1+y_2}{2}) \rightarrow (x_1, y_1) = (1, -2)$ and $(x_2, y_2) = (3, 6)$ <br><br> Midpoint $= (\frac{1+3}{2}, \frac{-2+6}{2}) \rightarrow (\frac{4}{2}, \frac{4}{2}) \rightarrow M(2, 2)$ |
| **Your Turn!** | 1) $(6, 0), (-4, 2)$ <br><br> *Midpoint* $= (1, 1)$ | 2) $(4, -1), (2, 3)$ <br><br> *Midpoint* $= (3, 1)$ |

| | | |
|---|---|---|
| 3) $(-3, 4), (-5, 0)$ <br><br> *Midpoint* $= (-4, 2)$ | 4) $(8, 1), (-4, 5)$ <br><br> *Midpoint* $= (2, 3)$ |
| 5) $(6, 7), (-4, 5)$ <br><br> *Midpoint* $= (1, 6)$ | 6) $(2, -3), (2, 5)$ <br><br> *Midpoint* $= (2, 1)$ |
| 7) $(7, 3), (-1, -7)$ <br><br> *Midpoint* $= (3, -2)$ | 8) $(3, 9), (-1, 5)$ <br><br> *Midpoint* $= (1, 7)$ |
| 9) $(3, 4), (-7, -6)$ <br><br> *Midpoint* $= (-2, -1)$ | 10) $(-5, 2), (11, -6)$ <br><br> *Midpoint* $= (3, -2)$ |

| Name: .......................................... | Date: .......................................... |
|---|---|

| **Topic** | **Finding Distance of Two Points** | |
|---|---|---|
| **Notes** | ✓ Use this formula to find the distance of two points A $(x_1, y_1)$ and B $(x_2, y_2)$: <br> $$d = \sqrt{(x_2 - x_1)^2 + (y_2 - y_1)^2}$$ | |
| **Example** | ***Find the distance of two points*** $(-1, 5)$ and $(4, -7)$. <br><br> **Solution:** *Use distance of two points formula:* $d =$ <br> $\sqrt{(x_2 - x_1)^2 + (y_2 - y_1)^2}$ <br> $(x_1, y_1) = (-1, 5)$, and $(x_2, y_2) = (4, -7)$ <br> Then: $d = \sqrt{(x_2 - x_1)^2 + (y_2 - y_1)^2} \rightarrow d =$ <br> $\sqrt{(4 - (-1))^2 + (-7 - 5)^2} = \sqrt{(-5)^2 + (-12)^2} = \sqrt{25 + 144} =$ <br> $\sqrt{169} = 13$ | |
| **Your Turn!** | 1) $(6, 2), (-4, 2)$ <br><br> *Distance* = ____ | 2) $(2, -3), (2, 5)$ <br><br> *Distance* = ____ |
| | 3) $(-5, 10), (7, 1)$ <br><br> *Distance* = ____ | 4) $(8, 1), (-4, 6)$ <br><br> *Distance* = ____ |
| | 5) $(-3, 6), (-4, 5)$ <br><br> *Distance* = ____ | 6) $(4, -1), (14, 23)$ <br><br> *Distance* = ____ |
| | 7) $(-3, 4), (-5, 0)$ <br><br> *Distance* = ____ | 8) $(3, 9), (-1, 5)$ <br><br> *Distance* = ____ |

| Name: ................................ | Date: ................................ |
|---|---|

| Topic | **Finding Distance of Two Points - Answers** |
|---|---|
| **Notes** | ✓ Use this formula to find the distance of two points A $(x_1, y_1)$ and B $(x_2, y_2)$:<br><br>$$d = \sqrt{(x_2 - x_1)^2 + (y_2 - y_1)^2}$$ |
| **Example** | *Find the distance of two points* $(-1,5)$ *and* $(4,-7)$.<br><br>**Solution: *Use distance of two points formula:*** $d = \sqrt{(x_2 - x_1)^2 + (y_2 - y_1)^2}$<br><br>$(x_1, y_1) = (-1, 5)$, and $(x_2, y_2) = (4, -7)$<br><br>Then: $d = \sqrt{(x_2 - x_1)^2 + (y_2 - y_1)^2} \to d =$<br><br>$\sqrt{(4 - (-1))^2 + (-7 - 5)^2} = \sqrt{(-5)^2 + (-12)^2} = \sqrt{25 + 144} =$<br><br>$\sqrt{169} = 13$ |

**Your Turn!**

| | |
|---|---|
| 1) $(6,2), (-4,2)$<br><br>**Distance** $= 10$ | 2) $(2,-3), (2,5)$<br><br>**Distance** $= 8$ |
| 3) $(-5,10), (7,1)$<br><br>**Distance** $= 15$ | 4) $(8,1), (-4,6)$<br><br>**Distance** $= 13$ |
| 5) $(-3,6), (-4,5)$<br><br>**Distance** $= \sqrt{2}$ | 6) $(4,-1), (14,23)$<br><br>**Distance** $= 26$ |
| 7) $(-3,4), (-5,0)$<br><br>**Distance** $= \sqrt{20} = 2\sqrt{5}$ | 8) $(3,9), (-1,5)$<br><br>**Distance** $= \sqrt{32} = 4\sqrt{2}$ |

| Name: .............................................. | Date: .............................................. |

| Topic | **Graphing Linear Inequalities** |
|-------|----------------------------------|
| **Notes** | ☑ To graph a linear inequality, first draw a graph of the "equals" line.<br>☑ Choose a testing point. (it can be any point on both sides of the line.)<br>☑ Put the value of $(x, y)$ of that point in the inequality. If that works, that part of the line is the solution. If the values don't work, then the other part of the line is the solution. |
| **Example** | **Sketch the graph of** $y < 3x + 2$<br><br>**Solution:** First, graph the line: $y = 3x + 2$<br><br>The slope is 3 and y-intercept is 2. Then, choose a testing point.<br><br>The easiest point to test is the origin: $(0, 0)$<br>$(0,0) \rightarrow y < 3x + 2 \rightarrow 0 < 3(0) + 2 \rightarrow 0 < 2$<br><br>0 is less than 2. So, this part of the line (on the right side) is the solution. |
| **Your Turn!** | 3) $y > 4x + 2$     4) $y < -2x + 5$ |

| Name: ............................................. | Date: ............................................. |

| Topic | **Graphing Linear Inequalities - Answers** |
|---|---|
| **Notes** | ☑ To graph a linear inequality, first draw a graph of the "equals" line. <br> ☑ Choose a testing point. (it can be any point on both sides of the line.) <br> ☑ Put the value of $(x, y)$ of that point in the inequality. If that works, that part of the line is the solution. If the values don't work, then the other part of the line is the solution. |
| **Example** | **Sketch the graph of** $y < 3x + 2$ <br><br> **Solution:** First, graph the line: $y = 3x + 2$ <br><br> The slope is 3 and y-intercept is 2. Then, choose a testing point. <br><br> The easiest point to test is the origin: $(0, 0)$ <br> $(0,0) \rightarrow y < 3x + 2 \rightarrow 0 < 3(0) + 2 \rightarrow 0 < 2$ <br><br> 0 is less than 2. So, this part of the line (on the right side) is the solution. <br><br> |
| **Your Turn!** | 1) $y > 4x + 2$     2) $y < -2x + 5$ <br>    |

| Name: ............................................... | Date: ........................................................ |

| Topic | **Multiplication Property of Exponents** | |
|---|---|---|
| **Notes** | ✓ Exponents are shorthand for repeated multiplication of the same number by itself. For example, instead of $2 \times 2$, we can write $2^2$. For $3 \times 3 \times 3 \times 3$, we can write $3^4$ <br> ✓ In algebra, a variable is a letter used to stand for a number. The most common letters are: $x, y, z, a, b, c, m, and\ n$. <br> ✓ Exponent's rules: $x^a \times x^b = x^{a+b}$ , $\frac{x^a}{x^b} = x^{a-b}$ <br> $\qquad (x^a)^b = x^{a \times b} \qquad\qquad (xy)^a = x^a \times y^a \qquad (\frac{a}{b})^c = \frac{a^c}{b^c}$ | |
| **Example** | **Multiply.** $4x^3 \times 2x^2$ <br><br> Use Exponent's rules: $x^a \times x^b = x^{a+b} \rightarrow x^3 \times x^2 = x^{3+2} = x^5$ <br> Then: $4x^3 \times 2x^2 = 8x^5$ | |
| **Your Turn!** | 1) $x^2 \times 3x =$ | 2) $5x^4 \times x^2 =$ |
| | 3) $3x^2 \times 4x^5 =$ | 4) $3x^2 \times 6xy =$ |
| | 5) $3x^5y \times 5x^2y^3 =$ | 6) $3x^2y^2 \times 5x^2y^8 =$ |
| | 7) $5x^2y \times 5x^2y^7 =$ | 8) $6x^6 \times 4x^9y^4 =$ |
| | 9) $8x^2y^5 \times 7x^5y^3 =$ | 10) $12x^6x^2 \times 3xy^5 =$ |

| Name: .......................................... | Date: .......................................... |
| --- | --- |

| **Topic** | **Multiplication Property of Exponents - Answers** | |
| --- | --- | --- |
| **Notes** | ✓ Exponents are shorthand for repeated multiplication of the same number by itself. For example, instead of $2 \times 2$, we can write $2^2$. For $3 \times 3 \times 3 \times 3$, we can write $3^4$ <br> ✓ In algebra, a variable is a letter used to stand for a number. The most common letters are: $x, y, z, a, b, c, m,$ and $n$. <br> ✓ Exponent's rules: $x^a \times x^b = x^{a+b}$ , $\dfrac{x^a}{x^b} = x^{a-b}$ <br> $\quad (x^a)^b = x^{a \times b} \qquad (xy)^a = x^a \times y^a \qquad \left(\dfrac{a}{b}\right)^c = \dfrac{a^c}{b^c}$ | | |
| **Example** | ***Multiply.*** $4x^3 \times 2x^2$ <br><br> Use Exponent's rules: $x^a \times x^b = x^{a+b} \rightarrow x^3 \times x^2 = x^{3+2} = x^5$ <br> Then: $4x^3 \times 2x^2 = 8x^5$ | | |
| **Your Turn!** | 1) $x^2 \times 3x = 3x^3$ | 2) $5x^4 \times x^2 = 5x^6$ |
| | 3) $3x^2 \times 4x^5 = 12x^7$ | 4) $3x^2 \times 6xy = 18x^3y$ |
| | 5) $3x^5y \times 5x^2y^3 = 15x^7y^4$ | 6) $3x^2y^2 \times 5x^2y^8 = 15x^4y^{10}$ |
| | 7) $5x^2y \times 5x^2y^7 = 25x^4y^8$ | 8) $6x^6 \times 4x^9y^4 = 24x^{15}y^4$ |
| | 9) $8x^2y^5 \times 7x^5y^3 = 56x^7y^8$ | 10) $12x^6x^7 \times 3xy^5 = 36x^9y^5$ |

| Name: .............................................. | Date: ........................................... |
|---|---|

| Topic | **Division Property of Exponents** |
|---|---|
| **Notes** | ✓ For division of exponents use these formulas: $\frac{x^a}{x^b} = x^{a-b}$ , $x \neq 0$ <br><br> $\frac{x^a}{x^b} = \frac{1}{x^{b-a}}$ , $x \neq 0,$ $\qquad \frac{1}{x^n} = x^{-n}$ |
| **Example** | **Simplify.** $\frac{6x^3y}{36x^2y^3}$ <br><br> First cancel the common factor: $6 \rightarrow \frac{6x^3y}{36x^2y^3} = \frac{x^3y}{6x^2y^3}$ <br><br> Use Exponent's rules: $\frac{x^a}{x^b} = x^{a-b} \rightarrow \frac{x^3}{x^2} = x^{3-2} = x^1 = x$ <br><br> Then: $\frac{6x^3y}{36x^2y^3} = \frac{xy}{9y^3} \rightarrow$ now cancel the common factor: $y \rightarrow \frac{xy}{6y^3} = \frac{x}{6y^2}$ |

| **Your Turn!** | 1) $\frac{3^7}{3^2} =$ | 2) $\frac{5x}{10x^3} =$ |
|---|---|---|
| | 3) $\frac{3x^3}{2x^5} =$ | 4) $\frac{12x^3}{14x^6} =$ |
| | 5) $\frac{12x^3}{9y^8} =$ | 6) $\frac{25xy^4}{5x^6y^2} =$ |
| | 7) $\frac{2x^4y^5}{7xy^2} =$ | 8) $\frac{16x^2y^8}{4x^3} =$ |
| | 9) $\frac{12x^4}{15x^7y^9} =$ | 10) $\frac{12yx^4}{10yx^8} =$ |

| Name: .................................................... | Date: .................................................... |

| Topic | **Division Property of Exponents - Answers** |
|---|---|
| **Notes** | ✓ For division of exponents use following formulas: $\frac{x^a}{x^b} = x^{a-b}$, $x \neq 0$ <br> $\frac{x^a}{x^b} = \frac{1}{x^{b-a}}$, $x \neq 0$, $\quad \frac{1}{x^b} = x^{-b}$ |
| **Example** | **Simplify.** $\frac{6x^3y}{36x^2y^3}$ <br><br> First cancel the common factor: $6 \rightarrow \frac{6x^3y}{36x^2y^3} = \frac{x^3y}{6x^2y^3}$ <br><br> Use Exponent's rules: $\frac{x^a}{x^b} = x^{a-b} \rightarrow \frac{x^3}{x^2} = x^{3-2} = x^1 = x$ <br><br> Then: $\frac{6x^3y}{36x^2y^3} = \frac{xy}{9y^3} \rightarrow$ now cancel the common factor: $y \rightarrow \frac{xy}{6y^3} = \frac{x}{6y^2}$ |

| **Your Turn!** | 1) $\frac{3^7}{3^2} = 3^5$ | 2) $\frac{5x}{10x^3} = \frac{1}{2x^2}$ |
|---|---|---|
| | 3) $\frac{3x^3}{2x^5} = \frac{3}{2x^2}$ | 4) $\frac{12x^3}{14x^6} = \frac{6}{7x^3}$ |
| | 5) $\frac{12x^3}{9y^8} = \frac{4x^3}{3y^8}$ | 6) $\frac{25xy^4}{5x^6y^2} = \frac{5y^2}{x^5}$ |
| | 7) $\frac{2x^4y^5}{7xy^2} = \frac{2x^3y^3}{7}$ | 8) $\frac{16x^2y^8}{4x^3} = \frac{4y^8}{x}$ |
| | 9) $\frac{12x^4}{15x^7y^9} = \frac{4}{5x^3y^9}$ | 10) $\frac{12y^8x^4}{10y^2x^8} = \frac{6y^6}{5x^4}$ |

| Name: ................................ | Date: ........................................ |
|---|---|

| **Topic** | **Powers of Products and Quotients** |
|---|---|
| **Notes** | ✓ For any nonzero numbers $a$ and $b$ and any integer $x$, $$(ab)^x = a^x \times b^x, \left(\frac{a}{b}\right)^c = \frac{a^c}{b^c}$$ |
| **Example** | **Simplify.** $\left(\frac{2x^3}{x}\right)^2$ <br><br> First cancel the common factor: $x \rightarrow \left(\frac{2x^3}{x}\right)^2 = (2x^2)^2$ <br><br> Use Exponent's rules: $(ab)^x = a^x \times b^x$ <br><br> Then: $(2x^2)^2 = (2)^2(x^2)^2 = 4x^4$ |

| **Your Turn!** | 1) $(4x^3x^3)^2 =$ | 2) $(3x^3 \times 5x)^2 =$ |
|---|---|---|
| | 3) $(10x^{11}y^3)^2 =$ | 4) $(9x^7y^5)^2 =$ |
| | 5) $(4x^4y^6)^3 =$ | 6) $(3x \times 4y^3)^2 =$ |
| | 7) $\left(\frac{5x}{x^2}\right)^2 =$ | 8) $\left(\frac{x^4y^4}{x^2y^2}\right)^3 =$ |
| | 9) $\left(\frac{25x}{5x^6}\right)^2 =$ | 10) $\left(\frac{x^8}{x^6y^2}\right)^2 =$ |

| Name: ........................... | Date: ............................... |

| Topic | **Powers of Products and Quotients - Answers** |
|---|---|
| **Notes** | ✓ For any nonzero numbers $a$ and $b$ and any integer $x$, $$(ab)^x = a^x \times b^x, (\frac{a}{b})^c = \frac{a^c}{b^b}$$ |
| **Example** | **Simplify.** $(\frac{2x^3}{x})^2$ <br><br> First cancel the common factor: $x \rightarrow (\frac{2x^3}{x})^2 = (2x^2)^2$ <br> Use Exponent's rules: $(ab)^x = a^x \times b^x$ <br> Then: $(2x^2)^2 = (2)^2(x^2)^2 = 4x^4$ |

| **Your Turn!** | 1) $(4x^3x^3)^2 = 16x^{12}$ | 2) $(3x^3 \times 5x)^2 = 225x^8$ |
|---|---|---|
| | 3) $(10x^{11}y^3)^2 = 100x^{22}y^6$ | 4) $(9x^7y^5)^2 = 81x^{14}y^{10}$ |
| | 5) $(4x^4y^6)^3 = 64\,x^{12}y^{18}$ | 6) $(3x \times 4y^3)^2 = 144x^2y^6$ |
| | 7) $(\frac{5x}{x^2})^2 = \frac{25}{x^2}$ | 8) $(\frac{x^4y^4}{x^2y^2})^3 = x^6y^6$ |
| | 9) $(\frac{25x}{5x^6})^2 = \frac{25}{x^{10}}$ | 10) $(\frac{x^8}{x^6y^2})^2 = \frac{x^4}{y^4}$ |

| Name: ............................................ | Date: ...................................................... |
|---|---|

| Topic | **Zero and Negative Exponents** |
|---|---|
| **Notes** | ✓ A negative exponent is the reciprocal of that number with a positive exponent. $(3)^{-2} = \frac{1}{3^2}$ <br><br> ✓ Zero-Exponent Rule: $a^0 = 1$, this means that anything raised to the zero power is 1. For example: $(28x^2y)^0 = 1$ |
| **Example** | *Evaluate.* $\left(\frac{1}{3}\right)^{-2} =$ <br><br> Use negative exponent's rule: $\left(\frac{1}{x^a}\right)^{-2} = (x^a)^2 \rightarrow \left(\frac{1}{3}\right)^{-2} = (3)^2 =$ <br> Then: $(3)^2 = 9$ |

| **Your Turn!** | 1) $2^{-3} =$ | 2) $3^{-3} =$ |
|---|---|---|
| | 3) $7^{-3} =$ | 4) $1^{-3} =$ |
| | 5) $8^{-3} =$ | 6) $4^{-4} =$ |
| | 7) $10^{-3} =$ | 8) $7^{-4} =$ |
| | 9) $\left(\frac{1}{8}\right)^{-1} =$ | 10) $\left(\frac{1}{5}\right)^{-2} =$ |

| Name: .................................... | Date: ........................................... |
|---|---|

| Topic | **Zero and Negative Exponents - Answers** |
|---|---|
| **Notes** | ✓ A negative exponent is the reciprocal of that number with a positive exponent. $(3)^{-2} = \frac{1}{??}$<br><br>✓ Zero-Exponent Rule: $a^0 = 1$, this means that anything raised to the zero power is 1. For example: $(28x^2y)^0 = 1$ |
| **Example** | *Evaluate.* $\left(\frac{1}{3}\right)^{-2} =$<br><br>Use negative exponent's rule: $\left(\frac{1}{x^a}\right)^{-2} = (x^a)^2 \rightarrow \left(\frac{1}{3}\right)^{-2} = (3)^2 =$<br>Then: $(3)^2 = 9$ |

| **Your Turn!** | | |
|---|---|---|
| | 1) $2^{-3} = \frac{1}{8}$ | 2) $3^{-3} = \frac{1}{27}$ |
| | 3) $7^{-3} = \frac{1}{343}$ | 4) $1^{-3} = 1$ |
| | 5) $8^{-3} = \frac{1}{512}$ | 6) $4^{-4} = \frac{1}{256}$ |
| | 7) $10^{-3} = \frac{1}{1,000}$ | 8) $7^{-4} = \frac{1}{2,401}$ |
| | 9) $\left(\frac{1}{8}\right)^{-1} = 8$ | 10) $\left(\frac{1}{5}\right)^{-2} = 25$ |

| Name: .................................... | Date: .................................... |
|---|---|

| Topic | **Negative Exponents and Negative Bases** | |
|---|---|---|
| **Notes** | ✓ Make the power positive. A negative exponent is the reciprocal of that number with a positive exponent. <br> ✓ The parenthesis is important! <br> $5^{-2}$ is not the same as $(\ 5\ )^{-2}$ <br><br> $(-\ 5)^{-2} = -\dfrac{1}{5^2}$ and $(-\ 5)^{-2} = +\dfrac{1}{5^2}$ | |
| **Example** | **Simplify.** $\left(-\dfrac{3x}{4yz}\right)^{-2} =$ <br><br> Use negative exponent's rule: $\left(\dfrac{x^a}{x^b}\right)^{-2} = \left(\dfrac{x^b}{x^a}\right)^2 \rightarrow \left(-\dfrac{3x}{4yz}\right)^{-3} = \left(-\dfrac{4y}{3x}\right)^3$ <br><br> Now use exponent's rule: $\left(\dfrac{a}{b}\right)^c = \dfrac{a^c}{b^c} \rightarrow \left(-\dfrac{4yz}{3x}\right)^3 = \dfrac{4^3 y^3 z^3}{3^3 x^3} = \dfrac{64 y^3 z^3}{27 x^3}$ | |
| **Your Turn!** | 1) $-5x^{-2}y^{-3} =$ | 2) $20x^{-4}y^{-1} =$ |
|  | 3) $14a^{-6}b^{-7} =$ | 4) $-12x^2 y^{-3} =$ |
|  | 5) $-\dfrac{25}{x^{-6}} =$ | 6) $\dfrac{7b}{-9c^{-4}} =$ |
|  | 7) $\dfrac{7ab}{a^{-3}b^{-1}} =$ | 8) $-\dfrac{5n^{-2}}{10p^{-3}} = -$ |
|  | 9) $\dfrac{4ab^{-2}}{-3c^{-2}} =$ | 10) $\left(\dfrac{3a}{2c}\right)^{-2} =$ |

| Name: .................................................. | Date: .............................................. |

| Topic | **Negative Exponents and Negative Bases - Answers** |
|---|---|
| **Notes** | ✓ Make the power positive. A negative exponent is the reciprocal of that number with a positive exponent.<br>✓ The parenthesis is important!<br>✓ $5^{-2}$ is not the same as $(-5)^{-2}$<br><br>$(-5)^{-2} = -\dfrac{1}{5^2}$ and $(-5)^{-2} = +\dfrac{1}{5^2}$ |
| **Example** | **Simplify.** $(-\dfrac{3x}{4yz})^{-2} =$<br><br>Use negative exponent's rule: $(\dfrac{x^a}{x^b})^{-2} = (\dfrac{x^b}{x^a})^2 \rightarrow (-\dfrac{3x}{4yz})^{-3} = (-\dfrac{4yz}{3x})^3$<br><br>Now use exponent's rule: $(\dfrac{a}{b})^c = \dfrac{a^c}{b^c} \rightarrow (-\dfrac{4yz}{3x})^3 = \dfrac{4^3 y^3 z^3}{3^3 x^3} = \dfrac{64 y^3 z^3}{27 x^3}$ |

| **Your Turn!** | 1) $-5x^{-2}y^{-3} = -\dfrac{5}{x^2 y^3}$ | 2) $20x^{-4}y^{-1} = \dfrac{20}{x^4 y}$ |
|---|---|---|
| | 3) $14a^{-6}b^{-7} = \dfrac{14}{a^6 b^7}$ | 4) $-12x^2 y^{-3} = -\dfrac{12x^2}{y^3}$ |
| | 5) $-\dfrac{25}{x^{-6}} = -25x^6$ | 6) $\dfrac{7b}{-9c^{-4}} = -\dfrac{7bc^4}{9}$ |
| | 7) $\dfrac{7ab}{a^{-3}b^{-1}} = 7a^4 b^2$ | 8) $-\dfrac{5n^{-2}}{10p^{-3}} = -\dfrac{p^3}{2n^2}$ |
| | 9) $\dfrac{4ab^{-2}}{-3c^{-2}} = -\dfrac{4ac^2}{3b^2}$ | 10) $(\dfrac{3a}{2c})^{-2} = \dfrac{4c^2}{9a^2}$ |

| Name: ................................................ | Date: ........................................................ |
|---|---|

| Topic | **Scientific Notation** |
|---|---|
| **Notes** | ✓ It is used to write very big or very small numbers in decimal form.<br>✓ In scientific notation all numbers are written in the form of:<br><br>$$m \times 10^n$$<br><br><table><tr><th>Decimal notation</th><th>Scientific notation</th></tr><tr><td>3</td><td>$3 \times 10^0$</td></tr><tr><td>– 45,000</td><td>$– 4.5 \times 10^4$</td></tr><tr><td>0.3</td><td>$3 \times 10^{-1}$</td></tr><tr><td>2,122.456</td><td>$2.122456 \times 10^3$</td></tr></table> |
| **Example** | **Write $0.00054$ in scientific notation.**<br><br>First, move the decimal point to the right so that you have a number that is between 1 and 10. Then: $m = 5.4$<br>Now, determine how many places the decimal moved in step 1 by the power of 10.<br>Then: $10^{-4} \rightarrow$ When the decimal moved to the right, the exponent is negative.<br>Then: $0.00054 = 5.4 \times 10^{-4}$ |

| **Your Turn!** | 1) $0.000325 =$ | 2) $0.000023 =$ |
|---|---|---|
| | 3) $52,000,000 =$ | 4) $21,000 =$ |
| | 5) $3 \times 10^{-1} =$ | 6) $5 \times 10^{-2} =$ |
| | 7) $1.2 \times 10^3 =$ | 8) $2 \times 10^{-4} =$ |

| Name: .......................................... | Date: .............................................. |

| Topic | **Scientific Notation - Answers** |
|---|---|

| **Notes** | ✓ It is used to write very big or very small numbers in decimal form.<br>✓ In scientific notation all numbers are written in the form of:<br><br>$$m \times 10^n$$<br><br>Decimal notation     Scientific notation<br><br>3         $3 \times 10^0$<br><br>$-45,000$     $-4.5 \times 10^4$<br>0.3       $3 \times 10^{-1}$<br><br>2,122.456    $2.122456 \times 10^3$ |

| **Example** | ***Write 0.00054 in scientific notation.***<br><br>First, move the decimal point to the right so that you have a number that is between 1 and 10. Then: $m = 5.4$<br>Now, determine how many places the decimal moved in step 1 by the power of 10.<br>Then: $10^{-4}$ → When the decimal moved to the right, the exponent is negative.<br>Then: $0.00054 = 5.4 \times 10^{-4}$ |

| **Your Turn!** | 1) $0.000325 = 3.25 \times 10^{-4}$ | 2) $0.00023 = 2.3 \times 10^{-5}$ |
|---|---|---|
| | 3) $52,000,000 = 5.2 \times 10^7$ | 4) $21,000 = 2.1 \times 10^4$ |
| | 5) $3 \times 10^{-1} = 0.3$ | 6) $5 \times 10^{-2} = 0.05$ |
| | 7) $1.2 \times 10^3 = 1,200$ | 8) $2 \times 10^{-4} = 0.0002$ |

| Name: .................................................. | Date: ............................................... |

| Topic | **Simplifying Polynomials** |
|---|---|
| **Notes** | ✓ Find "like" terms. (they have same variables with same power).<br><br>✓ Use "FOIL". (First–Out–In–Last) for binomials:<br><br>$(x + a)(x + b) = x^2 + (b + a)x + ab$<br><br>✓ Add or Subtract "like" terms using order of operation. |
| **Example** | ***Simplify this expression.*** $(x + 3)(x - 8) =$<br><br>**Solution:** First apply FOIL method: $(a + b)(c + d) = ac + ad + bc + bd$<br><br>$(x + 3)(x - 8) = x^2 - 8x + 3x - 24$<br><br>Now combine like terms: $x^2 - 8x + 3x - 24 = x^2 - 5x - 24$ |

| | |
|---|---|
| 1) $-(2x - 4) =$ | 2) $2(2x + 6) =$ |
| 3) $3x(3x - 4) =$ | 4) $5x(2x + 8) =$ |
| 5) $-2x(5x + 6) + 5x =$ | 6) $-4x(8x - 3) - x^2 =$ |
| 7) $(x + 4)(x + 5) =$ | 8) $(x + 2)(x + 8) =$ |
| 9) $-4x^2 + 10x^3 + 5x^2 =$ | 10) $-3x^5 + 10x^4 + 5x^5 =$ |

**Your Turn!**

| Name: ........................................ | Date: ........................................ |
|---|---|

| **Topic** | **Simplifying Polynomials - Answers** |
|---|---|
| **Notes** | ✓ Find "like" terms. (they have same variables with same power).<br><br>✓ Use "FOIL". (First–Out–In–Last) for binomials:<br><br>$$(x + a)(x + b) \quad x^2 + (b + a)x + ab$$<br><br>✓ Add or Subtract "like" terms using order of operation. |
| **Example** | **Simplify this expression.** $(x + 3)(x - 8) =$<br><br>**Solution:** First apply FOIL method: $(a + b)(c + d) = ac + ad + bc + bd$<br><br>$(x + 3)(x - 8) = x^2 - 8x + 3x - 24$<br><br>Now combine like terms: $x^2 - 8x + 3x - 24 = x^2 - 5x - 24$ |
| **Your Turn!** | 7) $-(2x - 4) =$<br>$\quad -2x + 4$ <br><br> 8) $2(2x + 6) =$<br>$\quad 4x + 12$ <br><br> 9) $3x(3x - 4) =$<br>$\quad 9x^2 - 12x$ <br><br> 10) $\quad 5x(2x + 8) =$<br>$\quad 10x^2 + 40x$ <br><br> 11) $\quad -2x(5x + 6) + 5x =$<br>$\quad -10x^2 - 7x$ <br><br> 12) $\quad -4x(8x - 3) - x^2 =$<br>$\quad -33x^2 + 12x$ <br><br> 11) $\quad (x + 4)(x + 5) =$<br>$\quad x^2 + 9x + 20$ <br><br> 12) $\quad (x + 2)(x + 8) =$<br>$\quad x^2 + 10x + 16$ <br><br> 13) $\quad -4x^2 + 10x^3 + 5x^2 =$<br>$\quad 10x^3 + x^2$ <br><br> 14) $-3x^5 + 10x^4 + 5x^5 =$<br>$\quad 2x^5 + 10x^4$ |

| Name: .................................................. | Date: .................................................. |
|---|---|

| **Topic** | **Adding and Subtracting Polynomials** |
|---|---|
| **Notes** | ✓ Adding polynomials is just a matter of combining like terms, with some order of operations considerations thrown in.<br>✓ Be careful with the minus signs, and don't confuse addition and multiplication! |
| **Example** | **Simplify the expressions.** $(3x^2 - 4x^3) - (5x^3 - 8x^2) =$<br><br>**Solution:** First use Distributive Property: $-(5x^3 - 8x^2) = -5x^3 + 8x^2$<br>$\rightarrow (3x^2 - 4x^3) - (5x^3 - 8x^2) = 3x^2 - 4x^3 - 5x^3 + 8x^2$<br>Now combine like terms: $3x^2 - 4x^3 - 5x^3 + 8x^2 = -9x^3 + 11x^2$ |

| **Your Turn!** | 1) $(x^2 - x) + (4x^2 - 5) =$<br><br>_____ | 2) $(2x^3 + x) - (x^3 + 2) =$<br><br>_____ |
|---|---|---|
| | 3) $(x^2 - 5x) + (6x^2 - 5) =$<br><br>_____ | 4) $(8x^2 - 2) - (3x^2 + 7) =$<br><br>_____ |
| | 5) $(3x^2 + 2) - (2 - 4x^2) =$<br><br>_____ | 6) $(x^3 + x^2) - (x^3 - 10) =$<br><br>_____ |
| | 7) $(3x^3 - 2x) - (x - x^3) =$<br><br>_____ | 8) $(x - 5x^4) - (2x^4 + 3x) =$<br><br>_____ |
| | 9) $(6x^3 + 5) - (4 - 5x^3) =$<br><br>_____ | 10) $(2x^2 + 5x^3) - (6x^3 + 7) =$<br><br>_____ |

| Name: .................................. | Date: ................................... |
|---|---|

| **Topic** | **Adding and Subtracting Polynomials - Answers** |
|---|---|
| **Notes** | ✓ Adding polynomials is just a matter of combining like terms, with some order of operations considerations thrown in. <br> ✓ Be careful with the minus signs, and don't confuse addition and multiplication! |
| **Example** | **Simplify the expressions.** $(3x^2 - 4x^3) - (5x^3 - 8x^2) =$ <br><br> **Solution:** First use Distributive Property: $-(5x^3 - 8x^2) = -5x^3 + 8x^2$ <br> $\rightarrow (3x^2 - 4x^3) - (5x^3 - 8x^2) = 3x^2 - 4x^3 - 5x^3 + 8x^2$ <br> Now combine like terms: $3x^2 - 4x^3 - 5x^3 + 8x^2 = -9x^3 + 11x^2$ |

| **Your Turn!** | | |
|---|---|---|
| | 1) $(x^2 - x) + (4x^2 - 5) =$ <br> $5x^2 - x - 5$ | 2) $(2x^3 + x) - (x^3 + 2) =$ <br> $x^3 + x - 2$ |
| | 3) $(x^2 - 5x) + (6x^2 - 5) =$ <br><br> $7x^2 - 5x - 5$ | 4) $(8x^2 - 2) - (3x^2 + 7) =$ <br> $5x^2 - 9$ |
| | 5) $(3x^2 + 2) - (2 - 4x^2) =$ <br> $7x^2$ | 6) $(x^3 + x^2) - (x^3 - 10) =$ <br> $x^2 + 10$ |
| | 7) $(3x^3 - 2x) - (x - x^3) =$ <br> $4x^3 - 3x$ | 8) $(x - 5x^4) - (2x^4 + 3x) =$ <br> $7x^4 - 2x$ |
| | 9) $(6x^3 + 5) - (4 - 5x^3) =$ <br> $11x^3 + 1$ | 10) $(2x^2 + 5x^3) - (6x^3 + 7) =$ <br> $-x^3 + 2x^2 - 7$ |

| Name: .............................................. | Date: .............................................. |

| Topic | **Multiplying Binomials** |
|---|---|
| **Notes** | ✓A binomial is a polynomial that is the sum or the difference of two terms, each of which is a monomial. <br> ✓To multiply two binomials, use "FOIL" method. (First–Out–In–Last) <br> $(x + a)(x + b) = x \times x + x \times b + a \times x + a \times b = x^2 + bx + ax + ab$ |
| **Example** | ***Multiply.*** $(x - 4)(x + 9) =$ <br><br> **Solution:** Use "FOIL". (First–Out–In–Last): $(x - 4)(x + 9) = x^2 + 9x - 4x - 36$ <br><br> Then simplify: $x^2 + 9x - 4x - 36 = x^2 + 5x - 36$ |

| **Your Turn!** | 1) $(x + 2)(x + 2) =$ <br><br> _____ | 2) $(x + 3)(x + 2) =$ <br><br> _____ |
|---|---|---|
| | 3) $(x - 3)(x + 4) =$ <br><br> _____ | 4) $(x - 2)(x - 4) =$ <br><br> _____ |
| | 5) $(x + 3)(x + 4) =$ <br><br> _____ | 6) $(x + 5)(x + 4) =$ <br><br> _____ |
| | 7) $(x - 6)(x - 5) =$ <br><br> _____ | 8) $(x - 5)(x - 5) =$ <br><br> _____ |
| | 9) $(x + 6)(x - 8) =$ <br><br> _____ | 10) $(x - 9)(x + 7) =$ <br><br> _____ |

| Name: ................................................ | Date: ................................................ |
|---|---|

| Topic | **Multiplying Binomials - Answers** |
|---|---|
| **Notes** | ✓ A binomial is a polynomial that is the sum or the difference of two terms, each of which is a monomial.<br>✓ To multiply two binomials, use "FOIL" method. (First–Out–In–Last)<br>$(x + a)(x + b) = x \times x + x \times b + a \times x + a \times b = x^2 + bx + ax + ab$ |
| **Example** | **Multiply.** $(x - 4)(x + 9) =$<br><br>**Solution:** Use "FOIL". (First–Out–In–Last): $(x - 4)(x + 9) = x^2 + 9x - 4x - 36$<br><br>Then simplify: $x^2 + 9x - 4x - 36 = x^2 + 5x - 36$ |

| | | |
|---|---|---|
| **Your Turn!** | 1) $(x + 2)(x + 2) =$<br>$x^2 + 4x + 4$ | 2) $(x + 3)(x + 2) =$<br>$x^2 + 5x + 6$ |
| | 3) $(x - 3)(x + 4) =$<br>$x^2 + x - 12$ | 4) $(x - 2)(x - 4) =$<br>$x^2 - 6x + 8$ |
| | 5) $(x + 3)(x + 4) =$<br>$x^2 + 7x + 12$ | 6) $(x + 5)(x + 4) =$<br>$x^2 + 9x + 20$ |
| | 7) $(x - 6)(x - 5) =$<br>$x^2 - 11x + 30$ | 8) $(x - 5)(x - 5) =$<br>$x^2 - 10x + 25$ |
| | 9) $(x + 6)(x - 8) =$<br>$x^2 - 2x - 48$ | 10) $(x - 9)(x + 7) =$<br>$x^2 - 2x - 63$ |

| Name: .................................... | Date: ............................... |
|---|---|

| **Topic** | **Multiplying and Dividing Monomials** |
|---|---|
| **Notes** | ✓ When you divide or multiply two monomials you need to divide or multiply their coefficients and then divide or multiply their variables.<br>✓ In case of exponents with the same base, you need to subtract their powers.<br>✓ Exponent's rules:<br><br>$$x^a \times x^b = x^{a+b}, \quad \frac{x^a}{x^b} = x^{a-b}$$<br>$$\frac{1}{x^b} = x^{-b}, \quad (x^a)^b = x^{a \times b}$$<br>$$(xy)^a = x^a \times y^a$$ |
| **Example** | *Divide expressions*. $\frac{-18x^5y^6}{2xy^2} =$<br><br>**Solution:** Use exponents' division rule: $\frac{x^a}{x^b} = x^{a-b}, \frac{x^5}{x} = x^{5-1} = x^4$ and<br>$\frac{y^6}{y^2} = y^4$<br><br>Then: $\frac{-18x^5y^6}{2xy^2} = -9x^4y^4$ |
| **Your Turn!** | 1) $(x^8y)(xy^2) =$<br><br>_____<br><br>3) $(x^7y^4)(2x^5y^2) =$<br><br>_____<br><br>5) $(-6x^8y^7)(4x^6y^9) =$<br><br>_____<br><br>7) $\frac{30x^8y^9}{6x^5y^4} =$<br><br>_____ | 2) $(x^4y^3)(x^2y^3) =$<br><br>_____<br><br>4) $(3x^5y^4)(4x^6y^3) =$<br><br>_____<br><br>6) $(-2x^9y^3)(9x^7y^8) =$<br><br>_____<br><br>8) $\frac{-42x^{12}y^{16}}{7x^8y^9} =$<br><br>_____ |

| Name: .................................... | Date: .................................... |
|---|---|

| Topic | **Multiplying and Dividing Monomials - Answers** |
|---|---|
| **Notes** | ✓ When you divide or multiply two monomials you need to divide or multiply their coefficients and then divide or multiply their variables.<br>✓ In case of exponents with the same base, you need to subtract their powers.<br>✓ Exponent's rules:<br><br>$$x^a \times x^b = x^{a+b}, \quad \frac{x^a}{x^b} = x^{a-b}$$<br>$$\frac{1}{x^b} = x^{-b}, \quad (x^a)^b = x^{a \times b}$$<br>$$(xy)^a = x^a \times y^a$$ |
| **Example** | **Divide expressions.** $\frac{-18x^5y^6}{2xy^2} =$<br><br>**Solution:** Use exponents' division rule: $\frac{x^a}{x^b} = x^{a-b}, \frac{x^5}{x} = x^{5-1} = x^4$ and<br>$\frac{y^6}{y^2} = y^4$<br><br>Then: $\frac{-18x^5y^6}{2xy^2} = -9x^4y^4$ |
| **Your Turn!** | 1) $(x^8 y)(xy^2) =$<br>$x^9 y^3$ <br><br> 2) $(x^4 y^3)(x^2 y^3) =$<br>$x^6 y^6$ <br><br> 3) $(x^7 y^4)(2x^5 y^2) =$<br>$2x^{12} y^6$ <br><br> 4) $(3x^5 y^4)(4x^6 y^3) =$<br>$12x^{11} y^7$ <br><br> 5) $(-6x^8 y^7)(4x^6 y^9) =$<br>$-24x^{14} y^{16}$ <br><br> 6) $(-2x^9 y^3)(9x^7 y^8) =$<br>$-18x^{16} y^{11}$ <br><br> 7) $\frac{30x^8 y^9}{6x^5 y^4} =$<br>$5x^3 y^5$ <br><br> 8) $\frac{12x^{12} y^{16}}{7x^8 y^9} =$<br>$-6x^4 y^7$ |

| Name: ................................. | Date: ................................. |
|---|---|

| Topic | **Multiplying a Polynomial and a Monomial** |
|---|---|
| **Notes** | ✓ When multiplying monomials, use the product rule for exponents. $x^a \times x^b = x^{a+b}$<br><br>✓ When multiplying a monomial by a polynomial, use the distributive property.<br><br>$$a \times (b + c) = a \times b + a \times c = ab + ac$$<br>$$a \times (b - c) = a \times b - a \times c = ab - ac$$ |
| **Example** | **Multiply expressions.** $4x(5x - 8) =$<br><br>**Solution:** Use Distributive Property: $4x(5x - 8) = 4x \times 5x - 4x \times (8) =$<br><br>Now, simplify: $4x \times 5x - 4x \times (8) = 20x^2 - 32x$ |
| **Your Turn!** | 1) $3x(2x + y) =$  _____     2) $x(x - 3y) =$  _____<br><br>3) $-x(5x - 3y) =$  _____     4) $4x(x + 5y) =$  _____<br><br>5) $-x(5x + 8y) =$  _____     6) $2x(6x - 7y) =$  _____<br><br>7) $-3x(x^3 + 4y^2 - 6x) =$  _____     8) $7x(x^2 - 5y^2 + 4) =$  _____ |

| Name: ............................................. | Date: ................................................. |
|---|---|

| Topic | **Multiplying a Polynomial and a Monomial - Answers** |
|---|---|
| **Notes** | ✓ When multiplying monomials, use the product rule for exponents. $x^a \times x^b = x^{a+b}$ <br><br> ✓ When multiplying a monomial by a polynomial, use the distributive property. <br><br> $$a \times (b + c) = a \times b + a \times c = ab + ac$$ $$a \times (b - c) = a \times b - a \times c = ab - ac$$ |
| **Example** | ***Multiply expressions.*** $4x(5x - 8) =$ <br><br> **Solution:** Use Distributive Property: $4x(5x - 8) = 4x \times 5x - 4x \times (8) =$ <br><br> Now, simplify: $4x \times 5x - 4x \times (8) = 20x^2 - 32x$ |

| Your Turn! | | |
|---|---|---|
| | 1) $3x(2x + y) =$ <br> $6x^2 + 3xy$ | 2) $x(x - 3y) =$ <br> $x^2 - 3xy$ |
| | 3) $-x(5x - 3y) =$ <br> $-5x^2 + 3xy$ | 4) $4x(x + 5y) =$ <br> $4x^2 + 20xy$ |
| | 5) $-x(5x + 8y) =$ <br> $-5x^2 - 8xy$ | 6) $2x(6x - 7y) =$ <br> $12x^2 - 14xy$ |
| | 7) $-3x(x^3 + 4y^2 - 6x) =$ <br> $-3x^4 - 12xy^2 + 18x^2$ | 8) $7x(x^2 - 5y^2 + 4) =$ <br> $7x^3 - 35xy^2 + 28x$ |

| Name: ............................................. | Date: ............................................. |
|---|---|

| Topic | **Multiplying Monomials** | |
|---|---|---|
| **Notes** | ✓ A monomial is a polynomial with just one term: Examples: $5x$ or $7x^2yz^8$. <br> ✓ When you multiply monomials, first multiply the coefficients (a number placed before and multiplying the variable) and then multiply the variables using multiplication property of exponents. $x^a \times x^b = x^{a+b}$ | |
| **Example** | *Multiply.* $(-3xy^4z^5) \times (2x^2y^5z^3) =$ <br><br> **Solution:** Multiply coefficients and find same variables and use multiplication property of exponents: $x^a \times x^b = x^{a+b}$ <br> $-3 \times 2 = -6$, $x \times x^2 = x^{1+2} = x^3$, $y^4 \times y^5 = y^{4+5} = y^9$, and $z^2 \times z^5 = z^{2+5} = z^7$ <br> Then: $(-3xy^4z^5) \times (2x^2y^5z^3) = -6x^3y^9z^7$ | |
| **Your Turn!** | 1) $2x^2 \times 4x^6 =$ <br> _____ | 2) $5x^7 \times 6x^4 =$ <br> _____ |
| | 3) $-2x^2y^4 \times 6x^3y^2 =$ <br> _____ | 4) $-5x^5y \times 3x^3y^4 =$ <br> _____ |
| | 5) $8x^7y^5 \times 5x^6y^3 =$ <br> _____ | 6) $-6x^7y^5 \times (-3x^9y^8) =$ <br> _____ |
| | 7) $12x^8y^8z^4 \times 3x^4y^3z =$ <br> _____ | 8) $-8x^9y^7z^{11} \times 7x^6y^7z^5 =$ <br> _____ |

| Name: ................................ | Date: ................................... |
|---|---|

| Topic | **Multiplying Monomials - Answers** |
|---|---|
| **Notes** | ✓ A monomial is a polynomial with just one term: Examples: **$5x$** or **$7x^2yz^8$**. <br> ✓ When you multiply monomials, first multiply the coefficients (a number placed before and multiplying the variable) and then multiply the variables using multiplication property of exponents. $x^a \times x^b = x^{a+b}$ |
| **Example** | **Multiply.** $(-3xy^4z^5) \times (2x^2y^5z^3) =$ <br><br> **Solution:** Multiply coefficients and find same variables and use multiplication property of exponents: $x^a \times x^b = x^{a+b}$ <br><br> $-3 \times 2 = -6$, $x \times x^2 = x^{1+2} = x^3$, $y^4 \times y^5 = y^{4+5} = y^9$, and $z^2 \times z^5 = z^{2+5} = z^7$ <br><br> Then: $(-3xy^4z^5) \times (2x^2y^5z^3) = -6x^3y^9z^7$ |

| **Your Turn!** | 1) $2x^2 \times 4x^6 =$ <br> $8x^8$ | 2) $5x^7 \times 6x^4 =$ <br> $30x^{11}$ |
|---|---|---|
| | 3) $-2x^2y^4 \times 6x^3y^2 =$ <br> $-12x^5y^6$ | 4) $-5x^5y \times 3x^3y^4 =$ <br> $-15x^8y^5$ |
| | 5) $8x^7y^5 \times 5x^6y^3 =$ <br> $40x^{13}y^8$ | 6) $-6x^7y^5 \times (-3x^9y^8) =$ <br> $18x^{16}y^{13}$ |
| | 7) $12x^8y^8z^4 \times 3x^4y^3z =$ <br> $36x^{12}y^{11}z^5$ | 8) $-8x^9y^7z^{11} \times 7x^6y^7z^5 =$ <br> $-56x^{15}y^{14}z^{16}$ |

| Name: ................................................ | Date: .................................................. |
|---|---|

| Topic | **Factoring Trinomials** |
|---|---|
| **Notes** | To factor trinomial, use of the following methods: <br> ✓ "FOIL": $(x + a)(x + b) = x^2 + (b + a)x + ab$ <br> ✓ "Difference of Squares": <br> $$a^2 - b^2 = (a + b)(a - b)$$ <br> $$a^2 + 2ab + b^2 = (a + b)(a + b)$$ <br> $$a^2 - 2ab + b^2 = (a - b)(a - b)$$ <br> ✓ "Reverse FOIL": $x^2 + (b + a)x + ab = (x + a)(x + b)$ |
| **Example** | ***Factor this trinomial.*** $x^2 + 12x + 32 =$ <br> **Solution:** Break the expression into groups: $(x^2 + 4x) + (8x + 32)$ <br> Now factor out $x$ from $x^2 + 4x$ : $x(x + 4)$ , and factor out 8 from $8x + 32$: <br> $8(x + 4)$ <br> Then: $(x^2 + 4x) + (8x + 32) = x(x + 4) + 8(x + 4)$ <br> Now factor out like term: $(x + 4) \rightarrow (x + 4)(x + 8)$ |

| **Your Turn!** | 1) $x^2 + 6x + 9 =$ <br><br> _____ | 2) $x^2 + 5x + 6 =$ <br><br> _____ |
|---|---|---|
| | 3) $x^2 + x + 12 =$ <br><br> _____ | 4) $x^2 - 6x + 8 =$ <br><br> _____ |
| | 5) $x^2 + 7x + 12 =$ <br><br> _____ | 6) $x^2 + 12x + 32 =$ <br><br> _____ |
| | 7) $x^2 - 11x + 30 =$ <br><br> _____ | 8) $x^2 - 14x + 45 =$ <br><br> _____ |

| Name: ................................. | Date: ..................................... |
|---|---|

| Topic | **Factoring Trinomials - Answers** | |
|---|---|---|
| **Notes** | To factor trinomial, use of the following methods:<br>✓ "FOIL": $(x + a)(x + b) = x^2 + (b + a)x + ab$<br>✓ "Difference of Squares":<br>$$a^2 - b^2 = (a + b)(a - b)$$<br>$$a^2 + 2ab + b^2 = (a + b)(a + b)$$<br>$$a^2 - 2ab + b^2 = (a - b)(a - b)$$<br>✓ "Reverse FOIL": $x^2 + (b + a)x + ab = (x + a)(x + b)$ | |
| **Example** | **Factor this trinomial.** $x^2 + 12x + 32 =$<br>**Solution:** Break the expression into groups: $(x^2 + 4x) + (8x + 32)$<br>Now factor out $x$ from $x^2 + 4x$ : $x(x + 4)$ , and factor out 8 from $8x + 32$:<br>$8(x + 4)$<br>Then: $(x^2 + 4x) + (8x + 32) = x(x + 4) + 8(x + 4)$<br>Now factor out like term: $(x + 4) \rightarrow (x + 4)(x + 8)$ | |
| **Your Turn!** | 1) $x^2 + 6x + 9 =$<br>$(x + 3)(x + 3)$ | 2) $x^2 + 5x + 6 =$<br>$(x + 3)(x + 2)$ |
| | 3) $x^2 + x + 12 =$<br>$(x - 3)(x + 4)$ | 4) $x^2 - 6x + 8 =$<br>$(x - 2)(x - 4)$ |
| | 5) $x^2 + 7x + 12 =$<br>$(x + 3)(x + 4)$ | 6) $x^2 + 12x + 32 =$<br>$(x + 8)(x + 4)$ |
| | 7) $x^2 - 11x + 30 =$<br>$(x - 6)(x - 5)$ | 8) $x^2 - 14x + 45 =$<br>$(x - 9)(x - 5)$ |

| Name: ................................... | Date: ......................................... |
|---|---|

| **Topic** | **Function Notation and Evaluation** |
|---|---|
| **Notes** | ✓ Functions are mathematical operations that assign unique outputs to given inputs.<br>✓ Function notation is the way a function is written. It is meant to be a precise way of giving information about the function without a rather lengthy written explanation.<br>✓ The most popular function notation is $f(x)$ which is read "$f$ of $x$".<br>✓ To evaluate a function, plug in the input (the given value or expression) for the function's variable (place holder, $x$). |
| **Example** | **Evaluate**: $h(n) = 2n^2 - 2$, find $h(2)$.<br><br>**Solution**: Substitute $n$ with 2:<br><br>Then: $h(n) = 2n^2 - 2 \rightarrow h(2) = 2(2)^2 - 2 = 8 - 2 \rightarrow h(2) = 6$ |

| **Your Turn!** | 1) $f(x) = x - 2$, find $f(-1)$<br><br>_____ | 2) $g(x) = 2x + 4$, find $g(3)$<br><br>_____ |
|---|---|---|
| | 3) $g(n) = 2n - 8$, find $g(-1)$<br><br>_____ | 4) $h(n) = n^2 - 1$, find $h(-2)$<br><br>_____ |
| | 5) $f(x) = x^2 + 12$, find $f(5)$<br><br>_____ | 6) $g(x) = 2x^2 - 9$, find<br><br>$g(-2)$<br><br>_____ |
| | 7) $w(x) = 2x^2 - 4x$, find $w(2n)$<br><br>_____ | 8) $p(x) = 4x^3 - 10$, find<br><br>$p(-3a)$<br><br>_____ |

| Name: .............................. | Date: .................................. |

| Topic | **Function Notation and Evaluation - Answers** |
|---|---|
| **Notes** | ✓ Functions are mathematical operations that assign unique outputs to given inputs.<br>✓ Function notation is the way a function is written. It is meant to be a precise way of giving information about the function without a rather lengthy written explanation.<br>✓ The most popular function notation is $f(x)$ which is read "$f$ of $x$".<br>✓ To evaluate a function, plug in the input (the given value or expression) for the function's variable (place holder, $x$). |
| **Example** | **Evaluate**: $h(n) = 2n^2 - 2$, find $h(2)$.<br><br>**Solution:** Substitute $n$ with 2:<br><br>Then: $h(n) = 2n^2 - 2 \rightarrow h(2) = 2(2)^2 - 2 = 8 - 2 \rightarrow h(2) = 6$ |

| | | |
|---|---|---|
| **Your Turn!** | 1) $f(x) = x - 2$, find $f(-1)$<br><br>$f(-1) = -3$ | 2) $g(x) = 2x + 4$, find $g(3)$<br><br>$g(3) = 10$ |
| | 3) $g(n) = 2n - 8$, find $g(-1)$<br><br>$g(-1) = -10$ | 4) $h(n) = n^2 - 1$, find $h(-2)$<br><br>$h(-2) = 3$ |
| | 5) $f(x) = x^2 + 12$, find $f(5)$<br><br>$f(5) = 37$ | 6) $g(x) = 2x^2 - 9$, find<br><br>$g(-2)$<br><br>$g(-2) = -1$ |
| | 7) $w(x) = 2x^2 - 4x$, find $w(2n)$<br><br>$w(2n) = 8n^2 - 8n$ | 8) $p(x) = 4x^3 - 10$, find<br><br>$p(-3a)$<br><br>$p(-3a) = -108a^3 + 30a$ |

| Name: ............................................ | Date: ............................................... |
|---|---|

| Topic | **Adding and Subtracting Functions** | |
|---|---|---|
| **Notes** | ✓ Just like we can add and subtract numbers and expressions, we can add or subtract two functions and simplify or evaluate them. The result is a new function. <br> ✓ For two functions $f(x)$ and $g(x)$, we can create two new functions: <br> $(f + g)(x) = f(x) + g(x)$ and $(f - g)(x) = f(x) - g(x)$ | |
| **Example** | $g(a) = 2a - 5, f(a) = a + 8$, Find: $(g + f)(a)$ <br><br> **Solution:** $(g + f)(a) = g(a) + f(a)$ <br><br> Then: $(g + f)(a) = (2a - 5) + (a + 8) = 3a + 3$ | |
| **Your Turn!** | 1) $g(x) = x - 2$ <br><br> $h(x) = 2x + 6$ <br> Find: $(h + g)(3)$ <br><br> _____ | 2) $f(x) = 3x + 2$ <br><br> $g(x) = -x - 6$ <br> Find: $(f + g)(2)$ <br><br> _____ |
| | 3) $f(x) = 5x + 8$ <br><br> $g(x) = 3x - 12$ <br> Find: $(f - g)(-2)$ <br><br> _____ | 4) $h(x) = 2x^2 - 10$ <br><br> $g(x) = 3x + 12$ <br> Find: $(h + g)(3)$ <br><br> _____ |
| | 5) $g(x) = 12x - 8$ <br><br> $h(x) = 3x^2 + 14$ <br> Find: $(h - g)(x)$ <br><br> _____ | 6) $h(x) = -2x^2 - 18$ <br><br> $g(x) = 4x^2 + 15$ <br> Find: $(h - g)(a)$ <br><br> _____ |

| Name: ............................................ | Date: ............................................ |

| Topic | **Adding and Subtracting Functions - Answers** | |
|---|---|---|
| **Notes** | ✓ Just like we can add and subtract numbers and expressions, we can add or subtract two functions and simplify or evaluate them. The result is a new function. <br> ✓ For two functions $f(x)$ and $g(x)$, we can create two new functions: <br> $(f + g)(x) = f(x) + g(x)$ and $(f - g)(x) = f(x) - g(x)$ | |
| **Example** | $g(a) = 2a - 5, f(a) = a + 8,$ Find: $(g + f)(a)$ <br><br> **Solution:** $(g + f)(a) = g(a) + f(a)$ <br><br> Then: $(g + f)(a) = (2a - 5) + (a + 8) = 3a + 3$ | |
| **Your Turn!** | 1) $g(x) = x - 2$ <br><br> $h(x) = 2x + 6$ <br> Find: $(h + g)(3)$ <br><br> 13 | 2) $f(x) = 3x + 2$ <br><br> $g(x) = -x - 6$ <br> Find: $(f + g)(2)$ <br><br> 0 |
| | 3) $f(x) = 5x + 8$ <br><br> $g(x) = 3x - 12$ <br> Find: $(f - g)(-2)$ <br><br> 16 | 4) $h(x) = 2x^2 - 10$ <br><br> $g(x) = 3x + 12$ <br> Find: $(h + g)(3)$ <br><br> 29 |
| | 5) $g(x) = 12x - 8$ <br><br> $h(x) = 3x^2 + 14$ <br> Find: $(h - g)(x)$ <br><br> $3x^2 - 12x + 22$ | 6) $h(x) = -2x^2 - 18$ <br><br> $g(x) = 4x^2 + 15$ <br> Find: $(h - g)(a)$ <br><br> $-6a^2 - 33$ |

| Name: ................................................ | Date: ................................................ |
|---|---|

| **Topic** | **Multiplying and Dividing Functions** | |
|---|---|---|
| **Notes** | ✓ Just like we can multiply and divide numbers and expressions, we can multiply and divide two functions and simplify or evaluate them. <br> ✓ For two functions $f(x)$ and $g(x)$, we can create two new functions: <br> $(f.g)(x) = f(x).g(x)$ and $\left(\frac{f}{g}\right)(x) = \frac{f(x)}{g(x)}$ | |
| **Example** | $g(x) = x + 5, f(x) = x - 3$, Find: $(g.f)(2)$ <br><br> **Solution:** $(g.f)(x) = g(x).f(x) = (x + 5)(x - 3) = x^2 - 3x + 5x - 15 = x^2 + 2x - 15$ <br><br> Substitute $x$ with 2: $(g.f)(x) = (2)^2 + 2(2) - 15 = 4 + 4 - 15 = -7$ | |
| **Your Turn!** | 1) $g(x) = x - 5$ <br><br> $h(x) = x + 6$ <br> Find: $(g.h)(-1)$ <br><br> _____ | 2) $f(x) = 2x + 2$ <br><br> $g(x) = -x - 6$ <br> Find: $\left(\frac{f}{g}\right)(-2)$ <br><br> _____ |
| | 3) $f(x) = 5x + 3$ <br><br> $g(x) = 2x - 4$ <br> Find: $\left(\frac{f}{g}\right)(5)$ <br><br> _____ | 4) $h(x) = x^2 - 2$ <br><br> $g(x) = x + 4$ <br> Find: $(g.h)(3)$ <br><br> _____ |
| | 5) $g(x) = 4x - 12$ <br><br> $h(x) = x^2 + 4$ <br> Find: $(g.h)(-2)$ <br><br> _____ | 6) $h(x) = 3x^2 - 8$ <br><br> $g(x) = 4x + 6$ <br> Find: $\left(\frac{f}{g}\right)(-4)$ <br><br> _____ |

| Name: ............................... | Date: ............................... |
|---|---|

| Topic | **Multiplying and Dividing Functions - Answers** | |
|---|---|---|
| **Notes** | ✓ Just like we can multiply and divide numbers and expressions, we can multiply and divide two functions and simplify or evaluate them.<br>✓ For two functions $f(x)$ and $g(x)$, we can create two new functions: $(f.g)(x) = f(x).g(x)$ and $\left(\frac{f}{g}\right)(x) = \frac{f(x)}{g(x)}$ | |
| **Example** | $g(x) = x + 5, f(x) = x - 3$, Find: $(g.f)(2)$<br><br>**Solution:** $(g.f)(x) = g(x).f(x) = (x + 5)(x - 3) = x^2 - 3x + 5x - 15 = x^2 + 2x - 15$<br><br>Substitute $x$ with 2: $(g.f)(x) = (2)^2 + 2(2) - 15 = 4 + 4 - 15 = -7$ | |
| **Your Turn!** | 1) $g(x) = x - 5$<br><br>$h(x) = x + 6$<br>Find: $(g.h)(-1)$<br><br>$(g.h)(-1) = -30$ | 2) $f(x) = 2x + 2$<br><br>$g(x) = -x - 6$<br>Find: $\left(\frac{f}{g}\right)(-2)$<br><br>$\left(\frac{f}{g}\right)(-2) = \frac{1}{2}$ |
| | 3) $f(x) = 5x + 3$<br><br>$g(x) = 2x - 4$<br>Find: $\left(\frac{f}{g}\right)(5)$<br><br>$\left(\frac{f}{g}\right)(5) = \frac{14}{3}$ | 4) $h(x) = x^2 - 2$<br><br>$g(x) = x + 4$<br>Find: $(g.h)(3)$<br><br>$(g.h)(3) = 49$ |
| | 5) $g(x) = 4x - 12$<br><br>$h(x) = x^2 + 4$<br>Find: $(g.h)(-2)$<br><br>$(g.h)(-2) = -160$ | 6) $h(x) = 3x^2 - 8$<br><br>$g(x) = 4x + 6$<br>Find: $\left(\frac{f}{g}\right)(-4)$<br><br>$\left(\frac{f}{g}\right)(-4) = -4$ |

| Name: ............................................... | | Date: .................................................... |
|---|---|---|

| **Topic** | **Composition of Functions** |
|---|---|
| **Notes** | ✓ "Composition of functions" simply means combining two or more functions in a way where the output from one function becomes the input for the next function.<br>✓ The notation used for composition is: $(f o g)(x) = f(g(x))$ and is read "$f$ composed with $g$ of $x$" or "$f$ of $g$ of $x$". |
| **Example** | **Using** $f(x) = x - 8$ **and** $g(x) = x + 2$, **find:** $(f \ o \ g)(3)$<br><br>**Solution:** $(f \ o \ g)(x) = f(g(x))$<br><br>**Then:** $(f \ o \ g)(x) = f(g(x)) = f(x + 2) = x + 2 - 8 = x - 6$<br><br>Substitute $x$ with 3: $(f \ o \ g)(3) = f(g(3)) = 3 - 6 = -3$ |
| **Your Turn!** | 1) $f(x) = 2x$<br><br>$g(x) = x + 3$<br>Find: $(fog)(2)$<br><br>_____    2) $f(x) = x + 2$<br><br>$g(x) = x - 6$<br>Find: $(fog)(-1)$<br><br>_____<br><br>3) $f(x) = 3x$<br><br>$g(x) = x + 4$<br>Find: $(gof)(4)$<br><br>_____    4) $h(x) = 2x - 2$<br><br>$g(x) = x + 4$<br>Find: $(goh)(2)$<br><br>_____<br><br>5) $f(x) = 2x - 8$<br><br>$g(x) = x + 10$<br>Find: $(fog)(-2)$<br><br>_____    6) $f(x) = x^2 - 8$<br><br>$g(x) = 2x + 3$<br>Find: $(gof)(4)$<br><br>_____ |

| Name: ................................ | | Date: ................................................ |
|---|---|---|

| Topic | Composition of Functions - Answers | |
|---|---|---|
| **Notes** | ✓ "Composition of functions" simply means combining two or more functions in a way where the output from one function becomes the input for the next function <br> ✓ The notation used for composition is: $(f o g)(x) = f(g(x))$ and is read "$f$ composed with $g$ of $x$" or "$f$ of $g$ of $x$". | |
| **Example** | ***Using*** $f(x) = x - 8$ ***and*** $g(x) = x + 2$, ***find:*** $(f\ o\ g)(3)$ <br><br> **Solution:** $(f\ o\ g)(x) = f(g(x))$ <br><br> *Then:* $(f\ o\ g)(x) = f(g(x)) = f(x + 2) = x + 2 - 8 = x - 6$ <br><br> Substitute $x$ with 3: $(f\ o\ g)(3) = f(g(3)) = 3 - 6 = -3$ | |
| **Your Turn!** | 1) $f(x) = 2x$ <br><br> $g(x) = x + 3$ <br> Find: $(fog)(2)$ <br><br> 10 | 2) $f(x) = x + 2$ <br><br> $g(x) = x - 6$ <br> Find: $(fog)(-1)$ <br><br> −5 |
| | 3) $f(x) = 3x$ <br><br> $g(x) = x + 4$ <br> Find: $(gof)(4)$ <br><br> 16 | 4) $h(x) = 2x - 2$ <br><br> $g(x) = x + 4$ <br> Find: $(goh)(2)$ <br><br> 6 |
| | 5) $f(x) = 2x - 8$ <br><br> $g(x) = x + 10$ <br> Find: $(fog)(-2)$ <br><br> 8 | 6) $f(x) = x^2 - 8$ <br><br> $g(x) = 2x + 3$ <br> Find: $(gof)(4)$ <br><br> 19 |

| Name: .............................................. | | Date: .............................................. |
|---|---|---|

| Topic | **Function Inverses** |
|---|---|

| **Notes** | ☑ An inverse function is a function that reverses another function: if the function $f$ applied to an input $x$ gives a result of $y$, then applying its inverse function $g$ to $y$ gives the result $x$. $f(x) = y$ if and only if $g(y) = x$ |
|---|---|

| **Example** | **1) *Find the inverse of*** f(x) = 4x + 2 <br> ***Solution: First, replace*** f(x) ***with*** y: y = 4x + 2 <br> ***Next, replace all*** x's ***with*** y ***and all*** y's ***with*** x: x = 4y + 2 <br> ***Now, solve for*** y: $x = 4y + 2 \rightarrow x - 2 = 4y \rightarrow \frac{1}{4}x - \frac{1}{2} = y$ <br> ***Finally replace*** y ***with*** f$^{-1}$(x): $f^{-1}(x) = \frac{1}{4}x - \frac{1}{2}$ <br><br> **2) Find the inverse of** $h(x) = \frac{x+1}{2}$ <br> **Solution:** $h(x) = \frac{x+1}{2} \rightarrow y = \frac{x+1}{2}$, ***replace all*** x's ***with*** y ***and all*** y's ***with*** x: $x = \frac{y+1}{2} \rightarrow 2x = y + 1 \rightarrow 2x - 1 = y \rightarrow h^{-1}(x) = 2x - 1$ |
|---|---|

| **Your Turn!** | **Find the inverse of each function.** |
|---|---|

| *1)* f(x) = $-\frac{1}{x}$ $- 9$ <br> $f^{-1}(x) =$ _____ | *2)* g(x) = $\sqrt{x} - 2$ <br> $g^{-1}(x) =$ _____ |
|---|---|
| *3)* h(x) = $-\frac{5}{x+3}$ <br> $h^{-1}(x) =$ _____ | *4)* f(x) = 6x + 6 <br> $f^{-1}(x) =$ _____ |

| Name: .................................. | | Date: .................................. |
|---|---|---|
| **Topic** | | **Function Inverses** |

| | |
|---|---|
| **Notes** | ☑ An inverse function is a function that reverses another function: if the function $f$ applied to an input $x$ gives a result of $y$, then applying its inverse function $g$ to $y$ gives the result $x$. $f(x) = y$ if and only if $g(y) = x$ |
| **Example** | **3)** *Find the inverse of* $f(x) = 4x + 2$ <br> *Solution: First, replace* $f(x)$ *with* $y$*:* $y = 4x + 2$ <br> *Next, replace all* $x's$ *with* $y$ *and all* $y's$ *with* $x$*:* $x = 4y + 2$ <br> *Now, solve for* $y$*:* $x = 4y + 2 \rightarrow x - 2 = 4y \rightarrow \frac{1}{4}x - \frac{1}{2} = y$ <br> *Finally replace* $y$ *with* $f^{-1}(x)$*:* $f^{-1}(x) = \frac{1}{4}x - \frac{1}{2}$ <br><br> **4)** Find the inverse of $h(x) = \frac{x+1}{2}$ <br> **Solution:** $h(x) = \frac{x+1}{2} \rightarrow y = \frac{x+1}{2}$*, replace all* $x's$ *with* $y$ *and all* $y's$ <br> **with** $x$*:* $x = \frac{y+1}{2} \rightarrow 2x = y + 1 \rightarrow 2x - 1 = y \rightarrow h^{-1}(x) = 2x - 1$ |
| **Your Turn!** | **Find the inverse of each function.** <br><br> *1)* $f(x) = -\frac{1}{x} - 9$    **\|**    *2)* $g(x) = \sqrt{x} - 2$ <br> $f^{-1}(x) = -\frac{1}{x+9}$    **\|**    $g^{-1}(x) = x^2 + 4x + 4$ <br><br> *3)* $h(x) = -\frac{5}{x+3}$    **\|**    *4)* $f(x) = 6x + 6$ <br> $h^{-1}(x) = -\frac{5}{x} - 3$    **\|**    $f^{-1}(x) = \frac{x-6}{6}$ |

| **Name:** ………………………………. | **Date:** ……………………………… |

| **Topic** | **Solving a Quadratic Equation** |
|---|---|
| **Notes** | ✓ Write the equation in the form of: $ax^2 + bx + c = 0$ <br> ✓ Factor the quadratic and solve for the variable. <br> ✓ Use quadratic formula if you couldn't factorize the quadratic. <br><br> ✓ Quadratic formula: $x = \dfrac{-b \pm \sqrt{b^2 - 4ac}}{2a}$ |
| **Example** | **Find the solutions of quadratic.** $x^2 + x - 72 = 0$ <br><br> **Solution:** Use quadratic formula: $x = \dfrac{-b \pm \sqrt{b^2 - 4ac}}{2a}$ , $a = 1, b = 1$ and $c = -72$ <br><br> $x = \dfrac{-1 \pm \sqrt{1^2 - 4 \times 1(-7\ )}}{2 \times 1}$ <br><br> $x_1 = \dfrac{-1 + \sqrt{1^2 - 4 \times 1 \times (-7\ )}}{2 \times 1} = 8$ , $x_2 = \dfrac{-1 - \sqrt{1^2 - 4 \times 1 \times (-72)}}{2 \times 1} = -9$ |

| **Your Turn!** | 1) $x^2 - x - 2 = 0$ <br><br> $x = \underline{\quad}, x = \underline{\quad}$ | 2) $x^2 - 6x + 8 = 0$ <br><br> $x = \underline{\quad}, x = \underline{\quad}$ |
|---|---|---|
| | 3) $x^2 - 4x + 3 = 0$ <br> $x = \underline{\quad}, x = \underline{\quad}$ | 4) $x^2 + x - 12 = 0$ <br> $x = \underline{\quad}, x = \underline{\quad}$ |
| | 5) $x^2 + 7x - 18 = 0$ <br> $x = \underline{\quad}, x = \underline{\quad}$ | 6) $x^2 - 2x - 15 = 0$ <br> $x = \underline{\quad}, x = \underline{\quad}$ |
| | 1) $x^2 + 6x - 40 = 0$ <br><br> $x = \underline{\quad}, x = \underline{\quad}$ | 2) $x^2 - 9x - 36 = 0$ <br><br> $x = \underline{\quad}, x = \underline{\quad}$ |

| Name: ............................................ | Date: ............................................. |
|---|---|

| **Topic** | **Solving a Quadratic Equation** |
|---|---|
| **Notes** | ✓ Write the equation in the form of: $ax^2 + bx + c = 0$<br>✓ Factor the quadratic and solve for the variable.<br>✓ Use quadratic formula if you couldn't factorize the quadratic.<br><br>✓ Quadratic formula: $x = \dfrac{-b \pm \sqrt{b^2 - 4ac}}{2a}$ |
| **Example** | **Find the solutions of quadratic.** $x^2 + x - 72 = 0$<br><br>**Solution:** Use quadratic formula: $x = \dfrac{-b \pm \sqrt{b^2 - 4ac}}{2a}$, $a = 1, b = 1$ and $c = -72$<br><br>$x = \dfrac{-1 \pm \sqrt{1^2 - 4 \times 1(-72)}}{2 \times 1}$<br><br>$x_1 = \dfrac{-1 + \sqrt{1^2 - 4 \times 1 \times (-72)}}{2 \times 1} = 8$ , $x_2 = \dfrac{-1 - \sqrt{1^2 - 4 \times 1 \times (-72)}}{2 \times 1} = -9$ |

| **Your Turn!** | 1) $x^2 - x - 2 = 0$<br><br>$x = 2, x = -1$ | 2) $x^2 - 6x + 8 = 0$<br><br>$x = 2, x = 4$ |
|---|---|---|
| | 3) $x^2 - 4x + 3 = 0$<br><br>$x = 3, x = 1$ | 4) $x^2 + x - 12 = 0$<br>$x = 3, x = -4$ |
| | 5) $x^2 + 7x - 18 = 0$<br><br>$x = 2, x = -9$ | 6) $x^2 - 2x - 15 = 0$<br>$x = 5, x = -3$ |
| | 7) $x^2 + 6x - 40 = 0$<br><br>$x = 4, x = -10$ | 8) $x^2 - 9x - 36 = 0$<br><br>$x = 12, x = -3$ |

| Name: ......................................... | Date: ............................................. |

| | |
|---|---|
| **Topic** | **Graphing Quadratic Functions** |
| **Notes** | ✓ Quadratic functions in vertex form: $y = a(x - h)^2 + k$ where $(h, k)$ is the vertex of the function. The axis of symmetry is $x = h$ <br> ✓ Quadratic functions in standard form: $y = ax^2 + bx + c$ where $x = -\frac{b}{2a}$ Is the value of $x$ in the vertex of the function. <br> ✓ To graph a quadratic function, first find the vertex, then substitute some values for $x$ and solve for $y$. |
| **Example** | ***Sketch the graph of*** $y = (x - 2)^2 - 5$ <br><br> **Solution:** <br> *The vertex of* $y = (x - 2)^2 - 5$ *is* $(2, 5)$. <br> Substitute zero for $x$ and solve for $y$. <br> $\qquad y = (0 - 2)^2 - 5 = -1$ <br> The $y$-*Intercept* is $(0, -1)$ <br> Now, you can simply graph the quadratic function. <br><br> |
| **Your Turn!** | 1) $y = (x - 4)^2 - 2$ <br><br> <br><br> 2) $y = 2(x + 2)^2 - 3$ <br><br> |

| Name: .................................... | Date: ...................................... |
|---|---|

| Topic | **Graphing Quadratic Functions** |
|---|---|
| **Notes** | ✓ Quadratic functions in vertex form: $y = a(x - h)^2 + k$ where $(h, k)$ is the vertex of the function. The axis of symmetry is $x = h$<br>✓ Quadratic functions in standard form: $y = ax^2 + bx + c$ where $x = -\frac{h}{2a}$ is the value of $x$ in the vertex of the function.<br>✓ To graph a quadratic function, first find the vertex, then substitute some values for $x$ and solve for $y$. |
| **Example** | **Sketch the graph of $y = (x - 2)^2 - 5$**<br><br>**Solution:**<br>*The vertex of $y = (x - 2)^2 - 5$ is $(2, 5)$.*<br>Substitute zero for $x$ and solve for $y$.<br>$$y = (0 - 2)^2 - 5 = -1$$<br>The *y-Intercept* is $(0, -1)$<br>Now, you can simply graph the quadratic function. 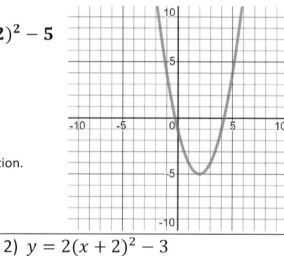 |
| **Your Turn!** | 1) $y = (x - 4)^2 - 2$ 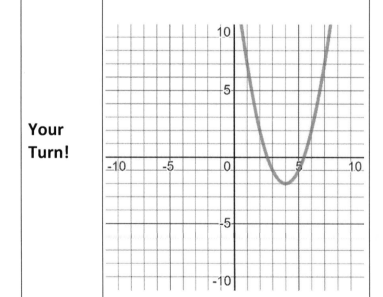    2) $y = 2(x + 2)^2 - 3$ 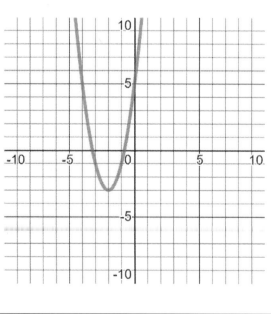 |

| Name: .................................... | Date: ..................................... |
|---|---|

| Topic | **Solving Quadratic Inequalities** |
|---|---|
| **Notes** | ✓ A quadratic inequality is one that can be written in the standard form of $ax^2 + bx + c > 0$ (or substitute $\leq, <,$ or $\geq$ for $>$). <br> ✓ Solving a quadratic inequality is like solving equations. We need to find the solutions (the zeroes). <br> ✓ To solve quadratic inequalities, first find quadratic equations. Then choose a test value between zeroes. Finally, find interval(s), such as $> 0$ or $< 0$. |
| **Example** | **Solve quadratic inequality.** $x^2 + x - 12 > 0$ <br><br> **Solution:** First solve $x^2 + x - 12 = 0$ by factoring. Then: $x^2 + x - 6 = 0 \rightarrow$ $(x - 3)(x + 4) = 0$. The product of two expressions is 0. Then: $(x - 3) = 0 \rightarrow x = 3$ or $(x + 4) = 0 \rightarrow x = -4$. Now, choose a value between 3 and $-4$. Let's choose 0. Then: $x = 0 \rightarrow x^2 + x - 12 > 0 \rightarrow (0)^2 + (0) - 12 > 0 \rightarrow -12 > 0$ <br> $-12$ is not greater than 0. Therefore, all values between 3 and $-4$ are NOT the solution of this quadratic inequality. The solution is: $x > 3$ and $x < -4$. |
| **Your Turn!** | 7) $x^2 - 6x - 27 > 0$ <br><br> _____ <br><br> 8) $x^2 + 13x + 42 < 0$ <br><br> _____ <br><br> 9) $x^2 + x - 56 > 0$ <br><br> _____ <br><br> 10) $x^2 - 15x + 54 < 0$ <br><br> _____ <br><br> 11) $x^2 + 2x - 35 \leq 0$ <br><br> _____ <br><br> 12) $x^2 - x - 72 \geq 0$ <br><br> _____ |

**Name:** ..................................  **Date:** ....................................

| Topic | Solving Quadratic Inequalities |
|-------|-------------------------------|
| **Notes** | ✓ A quadratic inequality is one that can be written in the standard form of $ax^2 + bx + c > 0$ (or substitute $<$, $\leq$, or $\geq$ for $>$). <br> ✓ Solving a quadratic inequality is like solving equations. We need to find the solutions (the zeroes). <br> ✓ To solve quadratic inequalities, first find quadratic equations. Then choose a test value between zeroes. Finally, find interval(s), such as $> 0$ or $< 0$. |
| **Example** | **Solve quadratic inequality.** $x^2 + x - 12 > 0$ <br><br> **Solution:** First solve $x^2 + x - 12 = 0$ by factoring. Then: $x^2 + x - 6 = 0 \rightarrow$ $(x - 3)(x + 4) = 0$. The product of two expressions is 0. Then: $(x - 3) = 0 \rightarrow x = 3$ or $(x + 4) = 0 \rightarrow x = -4$. Now, choose a value between 3 and $-4$. Let's choose 0. Then: $x = 0 \rightarrow x^2 + x - 12 > 0 \rightarrow (0)^2 + (0) - 12 > 0 \rightarrow -12 > 0$ $-12$ is not greater than 0. Therefore, all values between 3 and $-4$ are NOT the solution of this quadratic inequality. The solution is: $x > 3$ and $x < -4$. |
| **Your Turn!** | 1) $x^2 - 6x - 27 > 0$ <br><br> $x < -3 \ or \ x > 9$      2) $x^2 + 13x + 42 < 0$ <br><br> $-7 < x < -6$ <br><br> 3) $x^2 + x - 56 > 0$ <br> $x < -8 \ or \ x > 7$      4) $x^2 - 15x + 54 < 0$ <br> $6 < x < 9$ <br><br> 5) $x^2 + 2x - 35 \leq 0$ <br> $-7 \leq x \leq 5$      6) $x^2 - x - 72 \geq 0$ <br> $x \leq -8 \ or \ x \geq 9$ |

| Name: .......................................... | Date: .......................................... |

| Topic | **Graphing Quadratic Inequalities** |
|---|---|
| **Notes** | ✓ A quadratic inequality is in the form $y > ax^2 + bx + c$ (or substitute $<, \leq,$ or $>$ for $>$).<br>✓ To graph a quadratic inequality, start by graphing the quadratic parabola. Then fill in the region either inside or outside of it, depending on the inequality.<br>✓ Choose a testing point and check the solution section. |
| **Example** | **Sketch the graph of $y > x^2$**<br><br>**Solution:**<br>First, graph $y = x^2$<br>Since, the inequality sing is $>$, we need to use dash lines.<br>Now, choose a testing point inside the parabola. Let's choose $(0,2)$.<br>$y > x^2 \rightarrow 2 > (0)^2 \rightarrow 2 > 0$<br>This is true. So, inside the parabola is the solution section. |
| **Your Turn!** | 1) $y \leq x^2 + 4x + 5$      2) $y \leq x^2 + 2x - 3$ |

| Name: ................................................. | Date: ................................................. |

| Topic | **Graphing Quadratic Inequalities** |
|---|---|
| **Notes** | ✓ A quadratic inequality is in the form $y > ax^2 + bx + c$ (or substitute $<, \leq,$ or $\geq$ for $>$). <br> ✓ To graph a quadratic inequality, start by graphing the quadratic parabola. Then fill in the region either inside or outside of it, depending on the inequality. <br> ✓ Choose a testing point and check the solution section. |
| **Example** | **Sketch the graph of $y > x^2$** <br><br> **Solution:** <br> First, graph $y = x^2$ <br> Since, the inequality sing is $>$, we need to use dash lines. <br> Now, choose a testing point inside the parabola. Let's choose $(0,2)$. <br> $y > x^2 \rightarrow 2 > (0)^2 \rightarrow 2 > 0$ <br> This is true. So, inside the parabola is the solution section. <br> 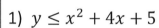 |
| **Your Turn!** | 1) $y \leq x^2 + 4x + 5$ <br><br> 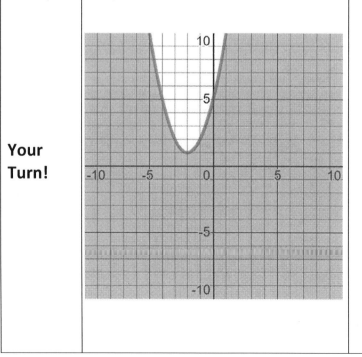 <br><br> 2) $y \leq x^2 + 2x - 3$ <br><br> 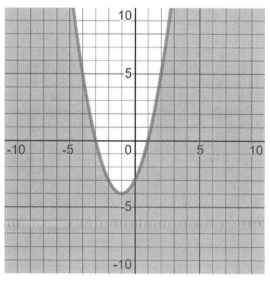 |

| Name: ............................................. | Date: ............................................. |
|---|---|

| Topic | **Adding and Subtracting Complex Numbers** |
|---|---|
| **Notes** | ✓ A complex number is expressed in the form $a + bi$, where $a$ and $b$ are real numbers, and $i$, which is called an imaginary number, is a solution of the equation $x^2 = -1$<br><br>✓ For adding complex numbers:<br><br>$$(a + bi) + (c + di) = (a + c) + (b + d)i$$<br><br>✓ For subtracting complex numbers:<br><br>$$(a + bi) - (c + di) = (a - c) + (b - d)i$$ |
| **Example** | Solve: $(14 + 7i) + (-5 - 3i)$<br><br>**Solution:** Remove parentheses: $(14 + 7i) + (-5 - 3i) \rightarrow 14 + 7i - 5 - 3i$<br><br>Combine like terms: $(14 - 5) + (7i - 3i) = 9 + 4i$ |

| | | |
|---|---|---|
| **Your Turn!** | 1) $(5 - 3i) - (4 + i) =$ <br><br>_____ | 2) $(2 + 6i) - (4 - 2i) =$ <br><br>_____ |
| | 3) $(7 + 4i) - (5 - 6i) =$ <br><br>_____ | 4) $(1 + 2i) + (5 - 7i) =$ <br><br>_____ |
| | 5) $(-8 + 2i) - (5 - 3i) =$ <br><br>_____ | 6) $(7 - 9i) - (3 + 5i) =$ <br><br>_____ |
| | 7) $(-9 - 3i) - (9 - 10i) =$ <br><br>_____ | 8) $(-12 - 4i) - (5 + 7i) =$ <br><br>_____ |

| Name: ................................ | Date: ..................................... |

| Topic | **Adding and Subtracting Complex Numbers** |
|-------|---------------------------------------------|
| **Notes** | ✓ A complex number is expressed in the form $a + bi$, where $a$ and $b$ are real numbers, and $i$, which is called an imaginary number, is a solution of the equation $x^2 = -1$ <br> ✓ For adding complex numbers: <br><br> $$(a + bi) + (c + di) = (a + c) + (b + d)i$$ <br> ✓ For subtracting complex numbers: <br><br> $$(a + bi) - (c + di) = (a - c) + (b - d)i$$ |
| **Example** | Solve: $(14 + 7i) + (-5 - 3i)$ <br><br> **Solution:** Remove parentheses: $(14 + 7i) + (-5 - 3i) \rightarrow 14 + 7i - 5 - 3i$ <br><br> Combine like terms: $(14 - 5) + (7i - 3i) = 9 + 4i$ |

| **Your Turn!** | 1) $(5 - 3i) - (4 + i) =$ <br><br> $1 - 4i$ | 2) $(2 + 6i) - (4 - 2i) =$ <br><br> $-2 + 6i$ |
|---|---|---|
| | 3) $(7 + 4i) - (5 - 6i) =$ <br><br> $2 + 10i$ | 4) $(1 + 2i) + (5 - 7i) =$ <br><br> $6 - 5i$ |
| | 5) $(-8 + 2i) - (5 - 3i) =$ <br><br> $-13 + 5i$ | 6) $(7 - 9i) - (3 + 5i) =$ <br><br> $4 - 14i$ |
| | 7) $(-9 - 3i) - (9 - 10i) -$ <br><br> $-18 + 7i$ | 8) $(-12 - 4i) - (5 + 7i) =$ <br><br> $-17 - 11i$ |

| Name: .......................................... | Date: .......................................... |
|---|---|

| Topic | **Multiplying and Dividing Complex Numbers** |
|---|---|
| **Notes** | ✓ Multiplying complex numbers: $(a + bi) + (c + di) = (ac - bd) + (ad + bc)i$<br><br>✓ Dividing complex numbers: $\frac{a+bi}{c+di} = \frac{a+bi}{c+di} \times \frac{c-di}{c-di} = \frac{ac+bd}{c^2+d^2} + \frac{bc-ad}{c^2+d^2} i$<br><br>✓ Imaginary number rule: $i^2 = -1$ |
| **Example** | **Solve:** $\frac{8-2i}{2+i}$<br><br>**Solution:** Use the rule for dividing complex numbers:<br><br>$$\frac{a+bi}{c+di} = \frac{a+bi}{c+di} \times \frac{c-di}{c-di} = \frac{ac+bd}{c^2+d^2} + \frac{bc-ad}{c^2+d^2} i \rightarrow$$<br><br>$$\frac{8-2i}{2+i} \times \frac{2-i}{2-i} = \frac{8 \times (2) + (-2)(1)}{2^2 + (1)^2} + \frac{-2 \times (2) - (8)(1)}{2^2 + (1)^2} i = \frac{14-12i}{5}$$<br><br>$$= \frac{14}{5} - \frac{12}{5} i$$ |

| **Your Turn!** | 1) $(2 - 2i)(4 - i) =$ <br><br> _____ | 2) $(3 - 2i)(2 - i) =$ <br><br> _____ |
|---|---|---|
| | 3) $(3 - i)(2 - 4i) =$ <br><br> _____ | 4) $(6 + i)(2 - 2i) =$ <br><br> _____ |
| | 5) $\frac{5-i}{6+i} =$ <br><br> _____ | 6) $\frac{7+2i}{3-2i} =$ <br><br> _____ |

**Name:** ............................................  **Date:** ...............................................

| Topic | **Multiplying and Dividing Complex Numbers** |
|---|---|
| **Notes** | ✓ Multiplying complex numbers: $(a + bi) + (c + di) = (ac - bd) + (ad + bc)i$ <br><br> ✓ Dividing complex numbers: $\frac{a+bi}{c+di} = \frac{a + bi}{c + di} \times \frac{c - di}{c - di} = \frac{ac + bd}{c^2 + d^2} + \frac{bc - ad}{c^2 + d^2} i$ <br><br> ✓ Imaginary number rule: $i^2 = -1$ |
| **Example** | **Solve:** $\frac{8-2i}{2+i}$ <br><br> **Solution:** Use the rule for dividing complex numbers: <br><br> $$\frac{a + bi}{c + di} = \frac{a + bi}{c + di} \times \frac{c - di}{c - di} = \frac{ac + bd}{c^2 + d^2} + \frac{bc - ad}{c^2 + d^2} i \rightarrow$$ <br><br> $$\frac{8 - 2i}{2 + i} \times \frac{2 - i}{2 - i} = \frac{8 \times (2) + (-2)(1)}{2^2 + (1)^2} + \frac{-2 \times (2) - (8)(1)}{2^2 + (1)^2} i = \frac{14 - 12i}{5}$$ <br><br> $$= \frac{14}{5} - \frac{12}{5} i$$ |
| **Your Turn!** | 1) $(2 - 2i)(4 - i) =$ <br><br> $6 - 10i$ <br><br><br> 2) $(3 - 2i)(2 - i) =$ <br><br> $4 - 7i$ <br><br><br> 3) $(3 - i)(2 - 4i) =$ <br><br> $2 - 14i$ <br><br><br> 4) $(6 + i)( 2 - 2i) =$ <br><br> $14 - 10i$ <br><br><br> 5) $\frac{5-i}{6+i} =$ <br><br> $\frac{29}{37} - \frac{11}{37} i$ <br><br><br> 6) $\frac{7+2i}{3-2i} =$ <br><br> $\frac{17}{13} + \frac{20}{13} i$ |

| Name: .............................................. | Date: .............................................. |
|---|---|

| Topic | **Rationalizing Imaginary Denominators** | |
|---|---|---|
| **Notes** | ✓  Step 1: Find the conjugate (it's the denominator with different sign between the two terms. <br><br> ✓  Step 2: Multiply numerator and denominator by the conjugate. <br><br> ✓  Step 3: Simplify if needed. | |
| **Example** | Solve: $\dfrac{6i}{3-3i}$ <br><br> **Solution:** First, divide both sides of the fraction by 3: $\dfrac{6i}{3-3i} = \dfrac{2i}{1-i}$ <br><br> Multiply both numerator and denominator by the conjugate $\dfrac{1+i}{1+i}$: $\dfrac{2i(1+i)}{(1-i)(1+i)} =$ <br><br> Apply complex arithmetic rule: $(a+bi)(a-bi) = a^2+b^2 \rightarrow (1-i)(1+i) =$ <br><br> $1^2 + (1)^2 = 2$, then: $\dfrac{2i(1+i)}{(1-i)(1+i)} = \dfrac{2i+2i^2}{2} = \dfrac{2i+2i^2}{2} = \dfrac{2i}{2} + \dfrac{2(-1)}{2} = -1+i$ | |
| **Your Turn!** | 1) $\dfrac{2-i}{3i} =$ <br><br> _____ | 2) $\dfrac{4i+1}{2+i} =$ <br><br> _____ |
| | 3) $\dfrac{6-3i}{3-i} =$ <br><br> _____ | 4) $\dfrac{8-3i}{2-i} =$ <br><br> _____ |
| | 5) $\dfrac{-8+2i}{6-3i} =$ <br><br> _____ | 6) $\dfrac{-9+4i}{2-3i} =$ <br><br> _____ |

| Name: ............................... | Date: ................................. |
|---|---|

| Topic | **Rationalizing Imaginary Denominators** |
|---|---|
| **Notes** | ✓ Step 1: Find the conjugate (it's the denominator with different sign between the two terms. <br> ✓ Step 2. Multiply numerator and denominator by the conjugate. <br> ✓ Step 3: Simplify if needed. |
| **Example** | Solve: $\dfrac{6i}{3-3i}$ <br><br> **Solution:** First, divide both sides of the fraction by 3: $\dfrac{6i}{3-3i} = \dfrac{2i}{1-i}$ <br><br> Multiply both numerator and denominator by the conjugate $\dfrac{1+i}{1+i}$: $\dfrac{2i(1+i)}{(1-i)(1+i)} =$ <br><br> Apply complex arithmetic rule: $(a+bi)(a-bi) = a^2 + b^2 \rightarrow (1-i)(1+i) =$ <br> $1^2 + (1)^2 = 2$, then: $\dfrac{2i(1+i)}{(1-i)(1+i)} = \dfrac{2i+2i^2}{2} = \dfrac{2i+2i^2}{2} = \dfrac{2i}{2} + \dfrac{2(-1)}{2} = -1+i$ |
| **Your Turn!** | 1) $\dfrac{2-i}{3i} =$    $\dfrac{1}{3} + \dfrac{2}{3}i$ <br><br> 2) $\dfrac{4i+1}{2+i} =$    $\dfrac{6}{5} + \dfrac{7}{5}i$ <br><br> 3) $\dfrac{6-3i}{3-i} =$    $\dfrac{21}{10} - \dfrac{3}{10}i$ <br><br> 4) $\dfrac{8-3i}{2-i} =$    $\dfrac{19}{5} + \dfrac{2}{5}i$ <br><br> 5) $\dfrac{-8+2i}{6-3i} =$    $-\dfrac{6}{5} - \dfrac{4}{15}i$ <br><br> 6) $\dfrac{-9+4i}{2-3i} =$    $-\dfrac{30}{13} - \dfrac{19}{13}i$ |

| Name: ............................................ | Date: ............................................... |
|---|---|

| **Topic** | **Simplifying Radical Expressions** |
|---|---|
| **Notes** | ☑ Find the prime factors of the numbers or expressions inside the radical.<br> ☑ Use radical properties to simplify the radical expression:<br><br> $\sqrt[n]{x^a} = x^{\frac{a}{n}}$, $\sqrt[n]{xy} = x^{\frac{1}{n}} \times y^{\frac{1}{n}}$, $\sqrt[n]{\dfrac{x}{y}} = \dfrac{x^{\frac{1}{n}}}{y^{\frac{1}{n}}}$, and $\sqrt[n]{x} \times \sqrt[n]{y} = \sqrt[n]{xy}$ |
| **Example** | Evaluate. $\sqrt{64} \times \sqrt{y^2} =$<br> First factor the numbers: $64 = 8^2$<br> Then: $\sqrt{64} \times \sqrt{y^2} = \sqrt{8^2} \times \sqrt{y^2}$<br> Now use radical rule: $\sqrt[n]{a^n} = a$, Then: $\sqrt{8^2} \times \sqrt{y^2} = 8 \times y = 8y$ |

| **Your Turn!** | 7) Evaluate. $\sqrt{49} =$<br><br>_____ | 8) Evaluate. $\sqrt{4} \times \sqrt{81} =$<br><br>_____ |
|---|---|---|
| | 9) Evaluate. $\sqrt{16} \times \sqrt{4x^2} =$<br><br>_____ | 10) Evaluate. $\sqrt{289} =$<br><br>_____ |
| | 11) Evaluate. $\sqrt{25b^4} =$<br><br>_____ | 12) Evaluate. $\sqrt{9} \times \sqrt{x^2} =$<br><br>_____ |

| Name: ............................................ | | Date: ............................................. |
|---|---|---|

| **Topic** | **Simplifying Radical Expressions** | |
|---|---|---|
| **Notes** | ☑ Find the prime factors of the numbers or expressions inside the radical. <br><br> ☑ Use radical properties to simplify the radical expression: <br><br> $\sqrt[n]{x^a} = x^{\frac{a}{n}}$, $\sqrt[n]{xy} = x^{\frac{1}{n}} \times y^{\frac{1}{n}}$, $\sqrt[n]{\frac{x}{y}} = \frac{x^{\frac{1}{n}}}{y^{\frac{1}{n}}}$, and $\sqrt[n]{x} \times \sqrt[n]{y} = \sqrt[n]{xy}$ | |
| **Example** | Evaluate. $\sqrt{64} \times \sqrt{y^2} =$ <br> First factor the numbers: $64 = 8^2$ <br> Then: $\sqrt{64} \times \sqrt{y^2} = \sqrt{8^2} \times \sqrt{y^2}$ <br> Now use radical rule: $\sqrt[n]{a^n} = a$, Then: $\sqrt{8^2} \times \sqrt{y^2} = 8 \times y = 8y$ | |
| **Your Turn!** | *1) Evaluate.* $\sqrt{49} = 7$ | *2) Evaluate.* $\sqrt{4} \times \sqrt{81} = 18$ |
| | *3) Evaluate.* $\sqrt{16} \times \sqrt{4x^2} = 8x$ | *4) Evaluate.* $\sqrt{289} = 17$ |
| | *5) Evaluate.* $\sqrt{25b^4} = 5b^2$ | *6) Evaluate.* $\sqrt{9} \times \sqrt{x^2} = 3x$ |

| Name: ................................................. | | Date: .................................................... |
|---|---|---|

| **Topic** | **Adding and Subtracting Radical Expressions** | |
|---|---|---|
| **Notes** | ☑ Only numbers that have the same radical part can be added or subtracted. <br><br> ☑ Remember, combining "unlike" radical terms is not possible. <br><br> ☑ For number with the same radical part, just add or subtract factors outside the radicals. | |
| **Example** | **1) Simplify.** $6\sqrt{5} + 3\sqrt{5}$ <br><br> Add like terms: $6\sqrt{5} + 3\sqrt{5} = 9\sqrt{5}$ <br><br> **2) Simplify.** $5\sqrt{7} - 3\sqrt{7}$ <br><br> Combine like terms: $5\sqrt{7} - 3\sqrt{7} = 2\sqrt{7}$ | |
| **Your Turn!** | **1) Simplify:** $\sqrt{6} + 6\sqrt{6} =$ <br><br> _____ | **2) Simplify:** $9\sqrt{8} - 6\sqrt{2} =$ <br><br> _____ |
| | **3) Simplify:** $-\sqrt{7} - 5\sqrt{7} =$ <br><br> _____ | **4) Simplify:** $10\sqrt{2} + 3\sqrt{18} =$ <br><br> _____ |
| | **5) Simplify:** $\sqrt{12} - 6\sqrt{3} =$ <br><br> _____ | **6) Simplify:** $-2\sqrt{x} + 6\sqrt{x} =$ <br><br> _____ |

| Name: ........................................ | Date: ........................................... |
|---|---|

| **Topic** | **Adding and Subtracting Radical Expressions** | |
|---|---|---|
| **Notes** | ☑ Only numbers that have the same radical part can be added or subtracted. <br><br> ☑ Remember, combining "unlike" radical terms is not possible. <br><br> ☑ For number with the same radical part, just add or subtract factors outside the radicals. | |
| **Example** | **1) Simplify.** $6\sqrt{5} + 3\sqrt{5}$ <br><br> Add like terms: $6\sqrt{5} + 3\sqrt{5} = 9\sqrt{5}$ <br><br> **2) Simplify.** $5\sqrt{7} - 3\sqrt{7}$ <br><br> Combine like terms: $5\sqrt{7} - 3\sqrt{7} = 2\sqrt{7}$ | |
| **Your Turn!** | *1) Simplify:* $\sqrt{6} + 6\sqrt{6} = 7\sqrt{6}$ | *2) Simplify:* $9\sqrt{8} - 6\sqrt{2} = 12\sqrt{2}$ |
| | *3) Simplify:* $-\sqrt{7} - 5\sqrt{7} = -6\sqrt{7}$ | *4) Simplify:* $10\sqrt{2} + 3\sqrt{18} = 19\sqrt{2}$ |
| | *5) Simplify:* $\sqrt{12} - 6\sqrt{3} =$ <br><br> $-4\sqrt{3}$ | *6) Simplify.* $-2\sqrt{x} + 6\sqrt{x} - 4\sqrt{x}$ |

| Name: ............................. | Date: ............................. |
|---|---|

| Topic | **Multiplying Rational Expressions** | |
|---|---|---|
| **Notes** | ✅ Multiplying rational expressions is the same as multiplying fractions. First, multiply numerators and then multiply denominators. Then, simplify as needed. | |
| **Examples** | 1) Solve: $\frac{x+5}{x-1} \times \frac{x-1}{3} =$ <br><br> Multiply fractions: $\frac{x+5}{x-1} \times \frac{x-1}{3} = \frac{(x+5)(x-1)}{3(x-1)}$ <br><br> Cancel the common factor: $(x-1)$, then: $\frac{(x+5)(x-1)}{3(x-1)} = \frac{(x+5)}{3}$ <br><br> 2) Solve $\frac{x-5}{x+4} \times \frac{2x+8}{x-5} =$ <br><br> Multiply fractions: $\frac{x-5}{x+4} \times \frac{2x+8}{x-5} = \frac{(x-5)(2x+8)}{(x+4)(x-5)}$ <br><br> Cancel the common factor: $\frac{(x-5)(2x+8)}{(x+4)(x-5)} = \frac{(2x+8)}{(x+4)}$ <br><br> Factor $2x+8 = 2(x+4)$, Then: $\frac{2(x+4)}{(x+4)} = 2$ | |
| **Your Turn!** | 1) $\frac{20x^3}{3} \times \frac{15}{4x} =$ _____ | 2) $\frac{x+6}{4} \times \frac{16}{x+6} =$ _____ |
| | 3) $\frac{x+10}{4x} \times \frac{3x}{7x+70} =$ _____ | 4) $\frac{x+8}{x+6} \times \frac{x-6}{4x+32} =$ _____ |

| Name: ..................................... | Date: ..................................... |
|---|---|

| **Topic** | **Multiplying Rational Expressions** |
|---|---|
| **Notes** | ☑ Multiplying rational expressions is the same as multiplying fractions. First, multiply numerators and then multiply denominators. Then, simplify as needed. |
| **Examples** | 1) Solve: $\dfrac{x+5}{x-1} \times \dfrac{x-1}{3} =$ <br><br> Multiply fractions: $\dfrac{x+5}{x-1} \times \dfrac{x-1}{3} = \dfrac{(x+5)(x-1)}{3(x-1)}$ <br><br> Cancel the common factor: $(x-1)$, then: $\dfrac{(x+5)(x-1)}{3(x-1)} = \dfrac{(x+5)}{3}$ <br><br> 2) Solve $\dfrac{x-5}{x+4} \times \dfrac{2x+8}{x-5} =$ <br><br> Multiply fractions: $\dfrac{x-5}{x+4} \times \dfrac{2x+8}{x-5} = \dfrac{(x-5)(2x+8)}{(x+4)(x-5)}$ <br><br> Cancel the common factor: $\dfrac{(x-5)(2x+8)}{(x+4)(x-5)} = \dfrac{(2x+8)}{(x+4)}$ <br><br> Factor $2x+8 = 2(x+4)$, Then: $\dfrac{2(x+4)}{(x+4)} = 2$ |
| **Your Turn!** | 1) $\dfrac{20x^3}{3} \times \dfrac{15}{4x} = 25x^2$     2) $\dfrac{x+6}{4} \times \dfrac{16}{x+6} = 4$ <br><br> 3) $\dfrac{x+10}{4x} \times \dfrac{3x}{7x+70} = \dfrac{3}{28}$     4) $\dfrac{x+8}{x+6} \times \dfrac{x-6}{4x+32} = \dfrac{x-6}{4(x+6)}$ |

| Name: .............................. | Date: .................................. |
| --- | --- |

| **Topic** | **Simplifying Radical Expressions Involving Fractions** | |
| --- | --- | --- |
| **Notes** | ☑ Radical expressions cannot be in the denominator. (number in the bottom) <br><br> ☑ To get rid of the radical in the denominator, multiply both numerator and denominator by the radical in the denominator. <br><br> ☑ If there is a radical and another integer in the denominator, multiply both numerator and denominator by the conjugate of the denominator. <br><br> ☑ The conjugate of a + b is a-b and vice versa. | |
| **Example** | **Simplify** $\dfrac{1}{\sqrt{5}-2}$ <br><br> Multiply by the conjugate: $\dfrac{\sqrt{5}+2}{\sqrt{5}+2}$ → $\dfrac{1}{\sqrt{5}-2} \times \dfrac{\sqrt{5}+2}{\sqrt{5}+2}$ <br><br> $(\sqrt{5}-2)(\sqrt{5}+2)=1$ then: $\dfrac{1}{\sqrt{5}-2} \times \dfrac{\sqrt{5}+2}{\sqrt{5}+2} = \dfrac{(\sqrt{5}+2)}{1} =$ <br> $\sqrt{5}+2$ | |
| **Your Turn!** | 13) *Simplify:* $\dfrac{1+\sqrt{5}}{1-\sqrt{3}} =$ <br><br> _____ | 14) *Simplify:* $\dfrac{2+\sqrt{6}}{\sqrt{2}-\sqrt{5}} =$ _____ |
| | 15) *Simplify:* $\dfrac{\sqrt{7}}{\sqrt{6}-\sqrt{3}} =$ <br><br> _____ | 16) *Simplify:* $\dfrac{\sqrt{8a}}{a^5} =$ _____ |

| Name: …………………………. | Date: ………………………………… |
|---|---|

| **Topic** | **Simplifying Radical Expressions Involving Fractions** | |
|---|---|---|
| **Notes** | ✓ Radical expressions cannot be in the denominator. (number in the bottom) <br><br> ✓ To get rid of the radical in the denominator, multiply both numerator and denominator by the radical in the denominator. <br><br> ✓ If there is a radical and another integer in the denominator, multiply both numerator and denominator by the conjugate of the denominator. <br><br> ✓ The conjugate of a + b is a-b and vice versa. | |
| **Example** | **Simplify** $\dfrac{1}{\sqrt{5}-2}$ <br><br> Multiply by the conjugate: $\dfrac{\sqrt{5}+2}{\sqrt{5}+2}$ $\rightarrow$ $\dfrac{1}{\sqrt{5}-2} \times \dfrac{\sqrt{5}+2}{\sqrt{5}+2}$ <br><br> $(\sqrt{5}-2)(\sqrt{5}+2) = 1$ then: $\dfrac{1}{\sqrt{5}-2} \times \dfrac{\sqrt{5}+2}{\sqrt{5}+2} = \dfrac{(\sqrt{5}+2)}{1} =$ $\sqrt{5}+2$ | |
| **Your Turn!** | *1) Simplify:* $\dfrac{1+\sqrt{5}}{1-\sqrt{3}} =$ <br><br> $\dfrac{(1+\sqrt{5})(1+\sqrt{3})}{2}$ | *2) Simplify:* $\dfrac{2+\sqrt{6}}{\sqrt{2}-\sqrt{5}} =$ <br><br> $\dfrac{2\sqrt{2}+2\sqrt{5}+2\sqrt{3}+\sqrt{30}}{3}$ |
| | *3) Simplify:* $\dfrac{\sqrt{7}}{\sqrt{6}-\sqrt{3}} = \dfrac{\sqrt{7}(\sqrt{6}+\sqrt{3})}{3}$ | *4) Simplify:* $\dfrac{\sqrt{8a}}{a^5} = \dfrac{2\sqrt{2}}{a^2}$ |

| Name: ............................................. | Date: ............................................. |
|---|---|

| Topic | Radical Equations |
|---|---|
| **Notes** | ☑ Isolate the radical on one side of the equation.<br><br>☑ Square both sides of the equation to remove the radical<br><br>☑ Solve the equation for the variable<br><br>☑ Plugin the answer into the original equation to avoid extraneous values. |
| **Example** | Solve $\sqrt{x} - 8 = -3$<br><br>Add 8 to both sides: $\sqrt{x} = 5$<br><br>Square both sides: $(\sqrt{x})^2 = 5^2 \rightarrow x = 25$<br><br>Substitute $x$ by 25 in the original equation and check the answer:<br><br>$$x = 25 \rightarrow \sqrt{x} - 8 = \sqrt{25} - 8 = -3$$<br><br>So, the value of 2 for $x$ is correct. |
| **Your Turn!** | 5) *Solve:* $2\sqrt{2x - 4} = 8$ <br><br>_____ <br><br> 6) *Solve:* $9 = \sqrt{4x - 1}$ <br><br>_____ <br><br> 7) *Solve:* $\sqrt{x} + 6 = 11$ <br><br>_____ <br><br> 8) *Solve:* $\sqrt{5x} = \sqrt{x + 3}$ <br><br>_____ |

| Name: ..................................... | Date: ..................................... |
|---|---|

| **Topic** | **Radical Equations** |
|---|---|
| **Notes** | ☑ Isolate the radical on one side of the equation.<br><br>☑ Square both sides of the equation to remove the radical<br><br>☑ Solve the equation for the variable<br><br>☑ Plugin the answer into the original equation to avoid extraneous values. |
| **Example** | Solve $\sqrt{x} - 8 = -3$<br><br>Add 8 to both sides: $\sqrt{x} = 5$<br><br>Square both sides: $(\sqrt{x})^2 = 5^2 \rightarrow x = 25$<br><br>Substitute $x$ by 25 in the original equation and check the answer:<br><br>$$x = 25 \rightarrow \sqrt{x} - 8 = \sqrt{25} - 8 = -3$$<br><br>So, the value of 2 for $x$ is correct. |

| **Your Turn!** | 1) Solve: $2\sqrt{2x - 4} = 8$<br><br>$x = 10$ | 2) Solve: $9 = \sqrt{4x - 1}$<br><br>$x = 20.5$ |
|---|---|---|
| | 3) Solve: $\sqrt{x} + 6 = 11$<br><br>$x = 25$ | 4) Solve: $\sqrt{5x} = \sqrt{x + 3}$<br><br>$x = \dfrac{3}{4}$ |

| Name: ................................ | | Date: ................................ |
|---|---|---|

| **Topic** | **Domain and Range of Radical Functions** | |
|---|---|---|
| **Notes** | ☑ To find the domain of the function, find all possible values of the variable inside radical.<br>☑ Remember that having a negative number under the square root symbol is not possible. (For cubic roots, we can have negative numbers)<br>☑ To find the range, plugin the minimum and maximum values of the variable inside radical. | |
| **Example** | Find the domain and range of the radical function.<br>$$y = \sqrt{x-8} + 5$$<br>For domain: Find non-negative values for radicals: $x - 8 \geq 0$<br>Then solve for $x$: $x - 8 \geq 0 \rightarrow x \geq 8$<br>Domain: $x \geq 8$<br>For range: the range of a radical function of the form<br>$c\sqrt{ax+b} + k$ is $f(x) \geq k$<br>$k = 5$, Then: $f(x) \geq 5$ | |
| **Your Turn!** | 1) *Identify the Domain and Range:*<br>$$y = \sqrt{x+1}$$ | 2) *Identify the Domain and Range:*<br>$$y = \sqrt{x-2} + 6$$ |
| | 3) *Sketch the graph of function:*<br>$$y = 2\sqrt{x} + 1$$<br> | 4) *Sketch the graph of function:*<br>$$y = \sqrt{x} + 5$$<br> |

| Name: ................................. | Date: ............................... |
|---|---|

| Topic | **Domain and Range of Radical Functions** |
|---|---|
| **Notes** | ✅ To find the domain of the function, find all possible values of the variable inside radical.<br>✅ Remember that having a negative number under the square root symbol is not possible. (For cubic roots, we can have negative numbers)<br>✅ To find the range, plugin the minimum and maximum values of the variable inside radical. |
| **Example** | Find the domain and range of the radical function.<br>$$y = \sqrt{x - 8} + 5$$<br>For domain: Find non-negative values for radicals: $x - 8 \geq 0$<br>Then solve for $x$: $x - 8 \geq 0 \rightarrow x \geq 8$<br>Domain: $x \geq 8$<br>For range: the range of a radical function of the form<br>$c\sqrt{ax + b} + k$ is $f(x) \geq k$<br>$k = 5$, Then: $f(x) \geq 5$ |

| **Your Turn!** | 1) *Identify the Domain and Range:*<br>$y = \sqrt{x + 1}, x \geq -1, y \geq 0$ | 2) *Identify the Domain and Range:*<br>$y = \sqrt{x - 2} + 6, x \geq 2, y \geq 6$ |
|---|---|---|
| | 3) *Sketch the graph of function:* $y = 2\sqrt{x} + 1$<br> | 4) *Sketch the graph of function:* $y = \sqrt{x} + 5$<br> |

| Name: .................................... | Date: .................................... |

| Topic | **Properties of Logarithms** |
|---|---|
| **Notes** | ☑ Learn some logarithms properties:<br><br>$a^{\log_a b} = b$ $\qquad\qquad$ $\log_a(x \cdot y) = \log_a x + \log_a y$<br><br>$\log_a 1 = 0$ $\qquad\qquad$ $\log_a \frac{x}{y} = \log_a x - \log_a y$<br><br>$\log_a a = 1$ $\qquad\qquad$ $\log_{x^k} x = \frac{1}{x} \log_a x, for\ k \neq 0$<br><br>$\log_a \frac{1}{x} = -\log_a x$ $\qquad\qquad$ $\log_a x^p = p\ \log_a x$<br><br>$\log_a x = \frac{1}{\log_x a}$ $\qquad\qquad$ $\log_a x = \log_{a^c} x^c$ |
| **Example** | Condense this expression to a single logarithm.<br>$$\log_b 2 - \log_b 7$$<br>**Solution:** Use log rule: $\log_a x - \log_a y = \log_a \frac{x}{y}$<br>Then: $\log_b 2 - \log_b 7 = \log_b \frac{2}{7}$ |
| **Your Turn!** | Condense this expression to a single logarithm.<br><br>17) $\log_a 5 - \log_a 8 =$ _____ $\qquad$ 18) $\log_x 3 - \log_x 5 =$ _____<br><br>19) $\log_b 2 + \log_b 3 =$ _____ $\qquad$ 20) $\log_a 7 + \log_a 2 =$ _____ |

| Name: ................................. | Date: ................................. |

| Topic | **Properties of Logarithms** |
|---|---|
| **Notes** | ☑ Learn some logarithms properties:<br><br>$a^{log_a b} = b$ $log_a(x \cdot y) = log_a x + log_a y$<br><br>$log_a 1 = 0$ $log_a \frac{x}{y} = log_a x - log_a y$<br><br>$log_a a = 1$ $log_{x^k} x = \frac{1}{x} log_a x, for \ k \neq 0$<br><br>$log_a \frac{1}{x} = -log_a x$ $log_a x^p = p \ log_a x$<br><br>$log_a x = \frac{1}{log_x a}$ $log_a x = log_{a^c} x^c$ |
| **Example** | Condense this expression to a single logarithm.<br><br>$$log \ 2 - log \ 7$$<br><br>**Solution:** Use log rule: $log_a x - log_a y = log_a \frac{x}{y}$<br><br>Then: $log \ 2 - log \ 7 = log \frac{2}{7}$ |

| | Condense this expression to a single logarithm. | |
|---|---|---|
| **Your Turn!** | 1) $log_a 5 - log \ 8 =$<br><br>$log_a \frac{5}{8}$ | 2) $log_x 3 - log_x 5 =$<br><br>$log_x \frac{3}{5}$ |
| | 3) $log_a 2 + log_b 3 =$<br><br>$log_b (6)$ | 4) $log_a 7 + log \ 2 =$<br><br>$log_a (11)$ |

| Name: ................................. | Date: ................................. |
|---|---|

| Topic | **Evaluating Logarithm** |
|---|---|
| **Notes** | ☑Logarithm is another way of writing exponent. $log_b{}^y = x$ is equivalent to $y = b^x$ <br><br> ☑Learn some logarithms rules: ($a > 0, a \neq 0, M > 0, N > 0$, and $k$ is a real number.) <br><br> Rule 1: $log_a(M.N) = log_a M + log_a N$,  Rule 2: $log_a \frac{M}{N} = log_a M - log_a N$ <br><br> Rule 3: $log_a(M)^k = k log_a M$,  Rule 4: $log_a a = 1$,  Rule 5: $log_a{}^1 = 0$ <br><br> Rule 6: $a^{log_a k} = k$ |
| **Example** | **Evaluate** $3log_2(8)$ <br><br> **Solution:** $8 = 2^3$, then $log_2(8) = log_2(2)^3$ <br><br> Use log rule: $log_a(M)^k = k log_a(M) \rightarrow log_2(2)^3 = 3 log_2(2)$ <br><br> Use log rule: $log_a(a) = 1 \rightarrow 3 \times 3 log_2{}^2 = 3 \times 3 = 9$ |
| **Your Turn!** | 21)  $2log_3(27) =$ _____   22)  $3log_4(256) =$ _____ <br><br> 23)  $\frac{1}{2} log_3(9) =$ _____   24)  $3log_5(25) =$ _____ <br><br> 25)  $6log_3(3) =$ _____   26)  $4log_6(1) =$ _____ |

| Name: ............................. | | Date: ............................. |
|---|---|---|

| **Topic** | **Evaluating Logarithm** | |
|---|---|---|
| **Notes** | ☑ Logarithm is another way of writing exponent. $log_b{}^y = x$ is equivalent to $y = b^x$.<br><br>☑ Learn some logarithms rules: ($a > 0, a \neq 0, M > 0, N > 0,$ and $k$ is a real number.)<br><br>Rule 1: $log_a(M.N) = log_aM + log_aN$,   Rule 2: $log_a\frac{M}{N} = log_aM - log_aN$<br><br>Rule 3: $log_a(M)^k = klog_aM$,   Rule 4: $log_aa = 1$,   Rule 5: $log_a{}^1 = 0$<br><br>Rule 6: $a^{log_ak} = k$ | |
| **Example** | **Evaluate** $3log_2(8)$<br><br>**Solution:** $8 = 2^3$, then $log_2(8) = log_2(2)^3$<br><br>Use log rule: $log_a(M)^k = klog_a(M) \rightarrow log_2(2)^3 = 3log_2(2)$<br><br>Use log rule: $log_a(a) = 1 \rightarrow 3 \times 3log_2{}^2 = 3 \times 3 = 9$ | |
| **Your Turn!** | 1) $2log_3(27) = 6$ | 2) $3log_4(256) = 12$ |
| | 3) $\frac{1}{2}log_3(9) = 1$ | 4) $3log_5(25) = 6$ |
| | 5) $6log_3(3) = 6$ | 6) $4log_6(1) = 0$ |

| Name: ................................. | | Date: ................................. |
|---|---|---|
| **Topic** | | **Natural Logarithms** |

| **Notes** | ☑ A natural logarithm is a logarithm that has a special base of the mathematical constant e, which is an irrational number approximately equal to 2.71. <br><br> ☑ The natural logarithm of $x$ is generally written as $ln\ x$, or $log_e\ x$. |
|---|---|

| **Example** | **Solve this equation for** x: $ln(3x - 4) = 1$ <br><br> **Solution:** Use $log$ rule: $a = log_b(b^a) \rightarrow 1 = ln(e^1) = ln(e) \rightarrow$ $ln(3x - 4) = ln\ (e)$ <br><br> When the logs have the same base: $log_b\big(f(x)\big) = log_b\big(g(x)\big) \rightarrow$ $f(x) = g(x)$ <br><br> $ln(3x - 4) = ln(e)$, then: $3x - 4 = e \rightarrow x = \frac{e+4}{3}$ |
|---|---|

| **Your Turn!** | 1) *Solve for x:* <br><br> $e^x = 36$ , $x =$ _____ | 2) *Solve for x:* <br><br> $ln\ x = 5, x =$ _____ |
|---|---|---|
| | 3) *Solve for x:* <br><br> $ln(2x - 3) = 1, x =$ _____ | 4) *Solve for x:* <br><br> $ln(ln\ x) = 2, x =$ _____ |
| | 5) *Reduce this expressions to simplest form:* $e^{ln\left(\frac{6}{e}\right)} =$ _____ | 6) *Reduce this expressions to simplest form:* $ln(\frac{1}{e})^3 =$ _____ |

| Name: ....................................... | | Date: ...................................... |
|---|---|---|

| **Topic** | **Natural Logarithms** |
|---|---|
| **Notes** | ☑ A natural logarithm is a logarithm that has a special base of the mathematical constant $e$, which is an irrational number approximately equal to 2.71.<br><br>☑ The natural logarithm of $x$ is generally written as $ln\ x$, or $log_e x$. |
| **Example** | **Solve this equation for** x: $ln(3x - 4) = 1$<br><br>**Solution:** Use *log* rule: $a = log_b(b^a) \rightarrow 1 = ln(e^1) = ln(e) \rightarrow ln(3x - 4) = ln\ (e)$<br><br>When the logs have the same base: $log_b\big(f(x)\big) = log_b\big(g(x)\big) \rightarrow f(x) = g(x)$<br><br>$ln(3x - 4) = ln(e)$, then: $3x - 4 = e \rightarrow x = \frac{e+4}{3}$ |

| **Your Turn!** | 1) *Solve for x:*<br><br>$e^x = 36, x = 2ln6$ | 2) *Solve for x:*<br><br>$ln\ x = 5, x = e^5$ |
|---|---|---|
| | 3) *Solve for x:*<br><br>$ln(2x - 3) = 1, x = \dfrac{e+3}{2}$ | 4) *Solve for x:*<br><br>$ln(ln\ x) = 2, x = e^{e^2}$ |
| | 5) *Reduce this expressions to simplest form:* $e^{ln\left(\frac{6}{e}\right)} = \dfrac{6}{e}$ | 6) *Reduce this expressions to simplest form:* $ln(\frac{1}{e})^3 = -3$ |

| Name: ................................ | Date: .................................... |
|---|---|

| Topic | **Solving Logarithmic Equations** |
|---|---|
| **Notes** | ☑ Convert the logarithmic equation to an exponential equation when it's possible. (If no base is indicated, the base of the logarithm is 10) <br><br> ☑ Condense logarithms if you have more than one log on one side of the equation. <br><br> ☑ Plug in the answers back into the original equation and check to see if the solution works. |
| **Example** | *Find the value of the variables in this equation.* $$log_2(25 - x^2) = 4$$ **Solution:** Use the logarithmic definition: $log_a(b) = c \rightarrow a^c = b$ $$log_2(25 - x^2) = 4 \rightarrow 2^4 = (25 - x^2) \rightarrow 16 = (25 - x^2)$$ Simplify: $16 = (25 - x^2) \rightarrow -x^2 + 25 - 16 = 0$ Then: $x^2 = 9 \rightarrow x = 3 \; or -3$ Both 3 and $-3$ work in the original equation. |

| | |
|---|---|
| **Your Turn!** | 1) *Find the value of $x$:* <br><br> $log_3 4x = 0 , x =$ _____ |

| 2) *Find the value of $x$:* <br><br> $logx + 4 = 1 , x =$ _____ |
|---|

| 3) *Find the value of $x$:* <br><br> $log3 - logx = 0 , x =$ ____ | 4) *Find the value of $x$:* <br><br> $log(x - 3) - log6 = 0 , x =$ ____ |
|---|---|

| Name: ................................................. | Date: ................................................. |
|---|---|

| Topic | **Solving Logarithmic Equations** |
|---|---|
| **Notes** | ☑ Convert the logarithmic equation to an exponential equation when it's possible. (If no base is indicated, the base of the logarithm is 10) <br><br> ☑ Condense logarithms if you have more than one log on one side of the equation. <br><br> ☑ Plug in the answers back into the original equation and check to see if the solution works. |
| **Example** | *Find the value of the variables in this equation.* <br><br> $$log_2(25 - x^2) = 4$$ <br> **Solution:** <br> Use the logarithmic definition: $log_a(b) = c \rightarrow a^c = b$ <br> $$log_2(25 - x^2) = 4 \rightarrow 2^4 = (25 - x^2) \rightarrow 16 = (25 - x^2)$$ <br> Simplify: $16 = (25 - x^2) \rightarrow -x^2 + 25 - 16 = 0$ <br> Then: $x^2 = 9 \rightarrow x = 3 \ or -3$ <br> Both $3$ and $-3$ work in the original equation. |

| | | |
|---|---|---|
| **Your Turn!** | 1) *Find the value of x:* <br><br> $log_3 4x = 0 , x = \dfrac{1}{4}$ | 2) *Find the value of x:* <br><br> $logx + 4 = 1 , x = \dfrac{1}{1000}$ |
| | 3) *Find the value of x:* <br><br> $log3 - logx = 0 , x = 3$ | 4) *Find the value of x:* <br><br> $log \ (x - 3) - log6 = 0 , x = 9$ |

| Name: .................................. | Date: .................................. |
|---|---|

| Topic | **Simplify Complex Fractions** |
|---|---|
| **Notes** | ☑ Convert mixed numbers to improper fractions.<br><br>☑ Simplify all fractions.<br><br>☑ Write the fraction in the numerator of the main fraction line then write division sing (÷) and the fraction of the denominator.<br><br>☑ Use normal method for dividing fractions.<br><br>☑ Simplify as needed. |
| **Example** | Solve: $\dfrac{\frac{2}{3}}{\frac{7}{10}-\frac{1}{4}}$<br><br>**Solution:** First, simplify the denominator: $\frac{7}{10}-\frac{1}{4}=\frac{9}{2-}$, Then: $\dfrac{\frac{2}{3}}{\frac{7}{10}-\frac{1}{4}}=\dfrac{\frac{2}{3}}{\frac{9}{20}}$<br><br>Now, write the complex fraction using the division sign (÷): $\dfrac{\frac{2}{3}}{\frac{9}{20}}=\frac{2}{3}\div\frac{9}{20}$<br><br>Use the dividing fractions rule: Keep, Change, Flip (keep the first fraction, change the division sign to multiplication, flip the second fraction)<br><br>$$\frac{2}{3}\div\frac{9}{20}=\frac{2}{3}\times\frac{20}{9}=\frac{40}{27}=1\frac{13}{27}$$ |
| **Your Turn!** | 1) $\dfrac{\frac{8}{3}}{\frac{2}{5}}=$ _____  $\qquad$ 2) $\dfrac{\frac{x}{3}+\frac{x}{8}}{\frac{1}{4}}=$ _____<br><br>3) $\dfrac{\frac{x+3}{3}}{\frac{x-2}{2}}=$ _____  $\qquad$ 4) $\dfrac{1+\frac{x}{4}}{x}=$ _____ |

| Name: .......................................... | Date: ................................... |
|---|---|

| Topic | **Simplify Complex Fractions** | |
|---|---|---|
| **Notes** | ☑ Convert mixed numbers to improper fractions.<br><br>☑ Simplify all fractions.<br><br>☑ Write the fraction in the numerator of the main fraction line then write division sing (÷) and the fraction of the denominator.<br><br>☑ Use normal method for dividing fractions.<br><br>☑ Simplify as needed. | |
| **Example** | Solve: $\dfrac{\frac{2}{3}}{\frac{7}{10}-\frac{1}{4}}$<br><br>**Solution:** First, simplify the denominator: $\dfrac{7}{10}-\dfrac{1}{4}=\dfrac{9}{2-}$, Then: $\dfrac{\frac{2}{3}}{\frac{7}{10}-\frac{1}{4}}=\dfrac{\frac{2}{3}}{\frac{9}{20}}$<br><br>Now, write the complex fraction using the division sign (÷): $\dfrac{\frac{2}{3}}{\frac{9}{20}}=\dfrac{2}{3}\div\dfrac{9}{20}$<br><br>Use the dividing fractions rule: Keep, Change, Flip (keep the first fraction, change the division sign to multiplication, flip the second fraction)<br><br>$$\dfrac{2}{3}\div\dfrac{9}{20}=\dfrac{2}{3}\times\dfrac{20}{9}=\dfrac{40}{27}=1\dfrac{13}{27}$$ | |
| **Your Turn!** | 1) $\dfrac{\frac{8}{3}}{\frac{2}{5}}=\dfrac{20}{3}$ | 2) $\dfrac{\frac{x}{3}+\frac{x}{8}}{\frac{1}{4}}=\dfrac{11x}{6}$ |
| | 3) $\dfrac{\frac{x+3}{3}}{\frac{x-2}{2}}=\dfrac{2x+6}{\text{∂N}~\text{6}}$ | 4) $\dfrac{1+\frac{x}{4}}{x}=\dfrac{4+x}{4x}$ |

| Name: ............................. | Date: ............................. |
|---|---|

| Topic | **Graphing Rational Expressions** |
|---|---|
| **Notes** | ☑ Find the vertical asymptotes of the function, if there is any. (Vertical asymptotes are vertical lines which correspond to the zeroes of the denominator) <br> ☑ Find horizontal or slant asymptote. (If numerator has a bigger degree than denominator, there will be slant asymptote.) <br> ☑ If denominator has a bigger degree than numerator, the horizontal asymptote is the $x$-axes or the line $y = 0$. If they have the same degree, the horizontal asymptote equals the leading coefficient (the coefficient of the largest exponent) of the numerator divided by the leading coefficient of the denominator. <br> ☑ Find intercepts and plug in some values of $x$ and solve for $y$ and graph. |
| **Example** | ***Graph rational expressions.*** $f(x) = \dfrac{3x}{x^2 - 2x}$ <br> **Solution:** First, notice that the graph is in two pieces. <br> Find $y - intercept$ by substituting zero for $x$ and solving for $y$ $(f(x))$: $x = 0 \rightarrow$ <br> $y = \dfrac{3x}{x^2 - 2x} = \dfrac{3(0)}{0^2 - 2(0)} = \dfrac{0}{0}, y -$ <br> $intercept: None$ <br> Asymptotes of $\dfrac{3x}{x^2 - 2x}$: vertical: $x = 2$, <br> Horizontal: $y = 0$ <br> After finding the asymptotes, you can plug in some values for $x$ and solve for $y$. Here is the sketch for this function. |
| **Your Turn!** | 1) ***Graph rational expressions.*** $f(x) = \dfrac{x^2 - 2x}{x - 3}$ | 2) ***Graph rational expressions.*** $f(x) = \dfrac{6x + 1}{x^2 - 4x}$ |

| Name: .................................. | Date: .................................. |
|---|---|

| Topic | Graphing Rational Expressions |
|---|---|

| Notes | ☑ Find the vertical asymptotes of the function, if there is any. (Vertical asymptotes are vertical lines which correspond to the zeroes of the denominator)<br>☑ Find horizontal or slant asymptote. (If numerator has a bigger degree than denominator, there will be slant asymptote.)<br>☑ If denominator has a bigger degree than numerator, the horizontal asymptote is the $x$-axes or the line $y = 0$. If they have the same degree, the horizontal asymptote equals the leading coefficient (the coefficient of the largest exponent) of the numerator divided by the leading coefficient of the denominator.<br>☑ Find intercepts and plug in some values of $x$ and solve for $y$ and graph. |
|---|---|

| Example | **Graph rational expressions.** $f(x) = \dfrac{3x}{x^2-2x}$<br>**Solution:** First, notice that the graph is in two pieces.<br>Find $y - intercept$ by substituting zero for $x$ and solving for $y$ $(f(x))$: $x = 0 \rightarrow$<br>$y = \dfrac{3x}{x^2-2x} = \dfrac{3(0)}{0^2-2(0)} = \dfrac{0}{0}, y -$<br>$intercept$: $None$<br>Asymptotes of $\dfrac{3x}{x^2-2x}$: vertical: $x = 2$,<br>Horizontal: $y = 0$<br>After finding the asymptotes, you can plug in some values for $x$ and solve for $y$. Here is the sketch for this function. |
|---|---|

| Your Turn! | 1) **Graph rational expressions.** $f(x) = \dfrac{x^2-2x}{x-3}$ | 2) **Graph rational expressions.** $f(x) = \dfrac{6x+1}{x^2-4x}$ |
|---|---|---|

| Name: ............................... | Date: ................................. |
|---|---|

| **Topic** | **Adding and Subtracting Rational Expressions** |
|---|---|
| **Notes** | For adding and subtracting rational expressions: <br><br> ☑ Find least common denominator (LCD). <br><br> ☑ Write each expression using the LCD. <br><br> ☑ Add or subtract the numerators. <br><br> ☑ Simplify as needed. |
| **Examples** | **1) Solve.** $\frac{3}{x+4} + \frac{x-2}{x+4} =$ <br><br> Use fraction addition rule: $\frac{a}{c} \pm \frac{b}{c} = \frac{a \pm b}{c} \rightarrow \frac{3}{x+4} + \frac{x-2}{x+4} = \frac{3+(x-2)}{x+4} =$ <br><br> $\frac{x+1}{x+4}$ <br><br> **2) Solve.** $\frac{x+4}{x-8} + \frac{x}{x+6} =$ <br> Least common denominator of $(x-8)$ and $(x+6)$: $(x-8)(x+6)$ <br> Then: $\frac{(x+4)(x+6)}{(x-8)(x+6)} + \frac{x(x-8)}{(x+6)(x-8)} = \frac{(x+4)(x+6)+x(x-8)}{(x+6)(x-6)}$ <br> Expand: $(x+4)(x+6) + x(x-8) = 2x^2 + 2x + 24$ <br> Then: $\frac{x+4}{x-8} + \frac{x}{x+6} = \frac{2x^2+2x+24}{(x+6)(x-8)}$ |
| **Your Turn!** | 1) $\frac{x+6}{x+1} - \frac{x+9}{x+1} =$ _____    2) $\frac{2x+1}{x+3} + \frac{2}{x+4} =$ _____ <br><br><br> 3) $\frac{14}{x+4} + \frac{6}{x^2-16} =$ _____    4) $\frac{x+2}{x+8} - \frac{2x}{x-8} =$ _____ |

Name: .............................................

Date: .............................................

| Topic | Adding and Subtracting Rational Expressions |
|---|---|
| **Notes** | For adding and subtracting rational expressions:<br><br>☑ Find least common denominator (LCD).<br>☑ Write each expression using the LCD.<br>☑ Add or subtract the numerators.<br>☑ Simplify as needed. |
| **Examples** | **1) Solve.** $\frac{3}{x+4} + \frac{x-2}{x+4} =$<br><br>Use fraction addition rule: $\frac{a}{c} \pm \frac{b}{c} = \frac{a \pm b}{c} \rightarrow \frac{3}{x+4} + \frac{x-2}{x+4} = \frac{3+(x-2)}{x+4} = \frac{x+1}{x+4}$<br><br>**2) Solve.** $\frac{x+4}{x-8} + \frac{x}{x+6} =$<br>Least common denominator of $(x-8)$ and $(x+6)$: $(x-8)(x+6)$<br>Then: $\frac{(x+4)(x+6)}{(x-8)(x+6)} + \frac{x(x-8)}{(x+6)(x-8)} = \frac{(x+4)(x+6)+x(x-8)}{(x+6)(x-6)}$<br>Expand: $(x+4)(x+6) + x(x-8) = 2x^2 + 2x + 24$<br>Then: $\frac{x+4}{x-8} + \frac{x}{x+6} = \frac{2x^2+2x+24}{(x+6)(x-8)}$ |
| **Your Turn!** | 1) $\frac{x+6}{x+1} - \frac{x+9}{x+1} = -\frac{3}{x+1}$     2) $\frac{2x+1}{x+3} + \frac{2}{x+4} = \frac{2x^2+11x+10}{(x+3)(x+4)}$ |
| | 3) $\frac{14}{x+4} + \frac{6}{x^2-16} = \frac{14x-50}{(x+4)(x-4)}$     4) $\frac{x+2}{x+8} - \frac{2x}{x-8} = \frac{-x^2-22x-16}{(x+8)(x-8)}$ |

| Topic | **Multiplying Rational Expressions** |
|---|---|

| Notes | ☑ Multiplying rational expressions is the same as multiplying fractions. First, multiply numerators and then multiply denominators. Then, simplify as needed. |
|---|---|

| Examples | 1) Solve: $\frac{x+5}{x-1} \times \frac{x-1}{3} =$ <br><br> Multiply fractions: $\frac{x+5}{x-1} \times \frac{x-1}{3} = \frac{(x+5)(x-1)}{3(x-1)}$ <br><br> Cancel the common factor: $(x-1)$, then: $\frac{(x+5)(x-1)}{3(x-1)} = \frac{(x+5)}{3}$ <br><br> 2) Solve $\frac{x-5}{x+4} \times \frac{2x+8}{x-5} =$ <br><br> Multiply fractions: $\frac{x-5}{x+4} \times \frac{2x+8}{x-5} = \frac{(x-5)(2x+8)}{(x+4)(x-5)}$ <br><br> Cancel the common factor: $\frac{(x-5)(2x+8)}{(x+4)(x-5)} = \frac{(2x+8)}{(x+4)}$ <br><br> Factor $2x+8 = 2(x+4)$, Then: $\frac{2(x+4)}{(x+4)} = 2$ |
|---|---|

| Your Turn! | 9) $\frac{20x^3}{3} \times \frac{15}{4x} =$ _____ | 10) $\frac{x+6}{4} \times \frac{16}{x+6} =$ _____ |
|---|---|---|
| | 11) $\frac{x+10}{4x} \times \frac{3x}{7x+70} =$ _____ | 12) $\frac{x+8}{x+6} \times \frac{x-6}{4x+32} =$ _____ |

| Name: ................................ | Date: ................................ |
|---|---|

| Topic | **Multiplying Rational Expressions** |
|---|---|
| **Notes** | ☑ Multiplying rational expressions is the same as multiplying fractions. First, multiply numerators and then multiply denominators. Then, simplify as needed. |

| **Examples** | 1) Solve: $\frac{x+5}{x-1} \times \frac{x-1}{3} =$ <br><br> Multiply fractions: $\frac{x+5}{x-1} \times \frac{x-1}{3} = \frac{(x+5)(x-1)}{3(x-1)}$ <br><br> Cancel the common factor: $(x-1)$, then: $\frac{(x+5)(x-1)}{3(x-1)} = \frac{(x+5)}{3}$ <br><br> 2) Solve $\frac{x-5}{x+4} \times \frac{2x+8}{x-5} =$ <br><br> Multiply fractions: $\frac{x-5}{x+4} \times \frac{2x+8}{x-5} = \frac{(x-5)(2x+8)}{(x+4)(x-5)}$ <br><br> Cancel the common factor: $\frac{(x-5)(2x+8)}{(x+4)(x-5)} = \frac{(2x+8)}{(x+4)}$ <br><br> Factor $2x+8 = 2(x+4)$, Then: $\frac{2(x+4)}{(x+4)} = 2$ |
|---|---|

| **Your Turn!** | 5) $\frac{20x^3}{3} \times \frac{15}{4x} = 25x^2$ | 6) $\frac{x+6}{4} \times \frac{16}{x+6} = 4$ |
|---|---|---|
|  | 7) $\frac{x+10}{4x} \times \frac{3x}{7x+70} = \frac{3}{28}$ | 8) $\frac{x+8}{x+6} \times \frac{x-6}{4x+32} = \frac{x-6}{4(x+6)}$ |

| Name: .................................. | Date: ................................ |
|---|---|

| Topic | **Dividing Rational Expressions** |
|---|---|
| **Notes** | ☑ To divide rational expression, use the same method we use for dividing fractions.<br>☑ Keep, Change, Flip<br>☑ Keep first rational expression, change division sign to multiplication, and flip the numerator and denominator of the second rational expression. Then, multiply numerators and multiply denominators. Simplify as needed. |
| **Example** | **Solve** $\dfrac{2x}{5} \div \dfrac{8}{7} =$<br><br>$\dfrac{2x}{5} \div \dfrac{8}{7} = \dfrac{\frac{2x}{5}}{\frac{8}{7}}$ , Use Divide fractions rules: $\dfrac{\frac{a}{b}}{\frac{c}{d}} = \dfrac{a.d}{b.c}$<br><br>$\dfrac{\frac{2x}{5}}{\frac{8}{7}} = \dfrac{2x \times 7}{8 \times 5} = \dfrac{14x}{40} = \dfrac{7x}{20}$<br><br>**Solve** $\dfrac{6x}{x+2} \div \dfrac{x}{6x+12} =$<br><br>$\dfrac{\frac{6x}{x+2}}{\frac{x}{6x+12}}$ , Use Divide fractions rules: $\dfrac{(6x)(6x+12)}{(x)(x+2)}$<br><br>Cancel common fraction: $\dfrac{(6x)(6x+12)}{(x)(x+2)} = \dfrac{36(x+2)}{(x+2)} = 36$ |
| **Your Turn!** | 5) $\dfrac{10x}{x+2} \div \dfrac{x}{60x+120} =$ _____     6) $\dfrac{5}{4} \div \dfrac{45}{8x} =$ _____<br><br>7) $\dfrac{x-6}{x+3} \div \dfrac{4}{x+3} =$ _____     8) $\dfrac{7x^3}{x^2-6} \div \dfrac{x^3}{x^2+x-56} =$ _____ |

| Name: ................................... | Date: ................................... |
|---|---|

| Topic | **Dividing Rational Expressions** | |
|---|---|---|
| **Notes** | ☑ To divide rational expression, use the same method we use for dividing fractions.<br>☑ Keep, Change, Flip<br>☑ Keep first rational expression, change division sign to multiplication, and flip the numerator and denominator of the second rational expression. Then, multiply numerators and multiply denominators. Simplify as needed. | |
| **Example** | **Solve** $\dfrac{2x}{5} \div \dfrac{8}{7} =$<br><br>$\dfrac{2x}{5} \div \dfrac{8}{7} = \dfrac{\frac{2x}{5}}{\frac{8}{7}}$ , Use Divide fractions rules: $\dfrac{\frac{a}{b}}{\frac{c}{d}} = \dfrac{a \cdot d}{b \cdot c}$<br><br>$\dfrac{\frac{2x}{5}}{\frac{8}{7}} = \dfrac{2x \times 7}{8 \times 5} = \dfrac{14x}{40} = \dfrac{7x}{20}$<br><br>**Solve** $\dfrac{6x}{x+2} \div \dfrac{x}{6x+12} =$<br><br>$\dfrac{\frac{6x}{x+2}}{\frac{x}{6x+12}}$ , Use Divide fractions rules: $\dfrac{(6x)(6x+12)}{(x)(x+2)}$<br><br>Cancel common fraction: $\dfrac{(6x)(6x+12)}{(x)(x+2)} = \dfrac{36(x+2)}{(x+2)} = 36$ | |
| **Your Turn!** | 13) $\dfrac{10x}{x+2} \div \dfrac{x}{60x+120} =$<br><br>$\qquad 600$ | 14) $\dfrac{5}{4} \div \dfrac{45}{8x} =$<br><br>$\qquad \dfrac{2x}{9}$ |
| | 15) $\dfrac{x-6}{x+3} \div \dfrac{4}{x+3} =$<br><br>$\qquad \dfrac{x-6}{4}$ | 16) $\dfrac{7x^3}{x^2-64} \div \dfrac{x^3}{x^2+x-56} =$<br><br>$\qquad \dfrac{7(x-7)}{x-8}$ |

| Name: ................................. | | Date: ................................. |
|---|---|---|

| **Topic** | **Rational Equations** | |
|---|---|---|
| **Notes** | For solving rational equations, we can use following methods:  ☑ Converting to a common denominator: In this method, you need to get a common denominator for both sides of the equation. Then make the numerators equal and solve for the variable.  ☑ Cross-multiplying: This method is useful when there is only one fraction on each side of the equation. Simply multiply the first numerator by the second denominator and make the result equal to the product of the second numerator and the first denominator. | |
| **Example** | Solve. $\dfrac{x-3}{x+1} = \dfrac{x+5}{x-2}$  Use cross multiply method: if $\dfrac{a}{b} = \dfrac{c}{d}$, then: $a \times d = b \times c$  Then: $(x-3)(x-2) = (x+5)(x+1)$  Expand: $(x-3)(x-2) = x^2 - 5x + 6$  Expand: $(x+5)(x+1) = x^2 + 6x + 5$, Then: $x^2 - 5x + 6 = x^2 + 6x + 5$, Simplify: $x^2 - 5x = x^2 + 6x - 1$  Subtract both sides $x^2 + 6x$ ,Then: $-11x = -1 \rightarrow x = \dfrac{1}{11}$ | |
| **Your Turn!** | 9) $\dfrac{1}{x^2} + \dfrac{4}{x} = \dfrac{6}{x}$    $x = \underline{\quad}$ | 10) $\dfrac{2}{x^2} - \dfrac{1}{x} = 1$    $x = \underline{\quad}$ |
| | 11) $\dfrac{x+1}{5x} - 1 = \dfrac{1}{x}$    $x = \underline{\quad}$ | 12) $\dfrac{6}{x} - \dfrac{1}{x} = \dfrac{1}{x^2+6x}$    $x = \underline{\quad}$ |

| Name: ......................... | Date: ............................... |
|---|---|

| **Topic** | **Rational Equations** |
|---|---|
| **Notes** | For solving rational equations, we can use following methods:<br><br>✅ Converting to a common denominator: In this method, you need to get a common denominator for both sides of the equation. Then make the numerators equal and solve for the variable.<br><br>✅ Cross-multiplying: This method is useful when there is only one fraction on each side of the equation. Simply multiply the first numerator by the second denominator and make the result equal to the product of the second numerator and the first denominator. |
| **Example** | Solve. $\frac{x-3}{x+1} = \frac{x+5}{x-2}$<br><br>Use cross multiply method: if $\frac{a}{b} = \frac{c}{d}$, then: $a \times d = b \times c$<br><br>Then: $(x-3)(x-2) = (x+5)(x+1)$<br><br>Expand: $(x-3)(x-2) = x^2 - 5x + 6$<br><br>Expand: $(x+5)(x+1) = x^2 + 6x + 5$, Then: $x^2 - 5x + 6 = x^2 + 6x + 5$, Simplify: $x^2 - 5x = x^2 + 6x - 1$<br><br>Subtract both sides $x^2 + 6x$, Then: $-11x = -1 \rightarrow x = \frac{1}{11}$ |

| **Your Turn!** | 1) $\frac{1}{x^2} + \frac{4}{x} = \frac{6}{x}$<br><br>$x = \frac{1}{2}$ | 2) $\frac{2}{x^2} - \frac{1}{x} = 1$<br><br>x = 1 or x = −2 |
|---|---|---|
| | 3) $\frac{x+1}{5x} - 1 = \frac{1}{x}$<br><br>x = −1 | 4) $\frac{6}{x} - \frac{1}{x} = \frac{1}{x^2+6x}$<br><br>$x = -\frac{29}{5}$ |

| Name: ................................ | | Date: .................................... |
|---|---|---|

| **Topic** | **Arithmetic Sequences** |
|---|---|

| **Notes** | ☑ A sequence of numbers such that the difference between the consecutive terms is constant is called arithmetic sequence. For example, the sequence 6, 8, 10, 12, 14, … is an arithmetic sequence with common difference of 2.<br><br>☑ To find any term in an arithmetic sequence use this formula: $x_n = a + d(n-1)$<br><br>$a$ = the first term,   $d$ = the common difference between terms, $n$ = number of items |
|---|---|

| **Example** | **Find the first five terms of the sequence.** $a_{10} = 92, d = 4$<br><br>**Solution:** First, we need to find $a_1$ *or* $a$. Use arithmetic sequence formula:<br><br>$x_n = a + d(n-1)$<br><br>If $a_{10} = 92$, then $n = 10$. Rewrite the formula and put the values provided:<br><br>$x_n = a + d(n-1) \rightarrow 92 = a + 4(10-1) = a + 36$, now solve for $a$.<br><br>$92 = a + 36 \rightarrow a = 92 - 36 = 56$,<br><br>First Five Terms: $56, 60, 64, 68, 72$ |
|---|---|

| **Your Turn!** | **Find the first five terms of the sequences.** |
|---|---|

| | |
|---|---|
| 1) $a_{12} = 122, d = 8$<br><br>___, ___, ___, ___, ___ | 2) $a_{14} = 240, d = 6$<br><br>___, ___, ___, ___, ___ |
| 3) $a_{15} = 216, d = 3$<br><br>___, ___, ___, ___, ___ | 4) $a_{20} = 280, d = 10$<br><br>___, ___, ___, ___, ___ |

| Name: ................................ | Date: ................................ |
|---|---|

| **Topic** | **Arithmetic Sequences** |
|---|---|
| **Notes** | ☑ A sequence of numbers such that the difference between the consecutive terms is constant is called arithmetic sequence. For example, the sequence 6, 8, 10, 12, 14, ... is an arithmetic sequence with common difference of 2.<br>☑ To find any term in an arithmetic sequence use this formula: $x_n = a + d(n-1)$<br> $a$ = the first term, $\quad d$ = the common difference between terms, $n$ = number of items |
| **Example** | **Find the first five terms of the sequence.** $a_{10} = 92, d = 4$<br>**Solution:** First, we need to find $a_1 \ or \ a$. Use arithmetic sequence formula:<br>$x_n = a + d(n-1)$<br>If $a_{10} = 92$, then $n = 10$. Rewrite the formula and put the values provided:<br>$x_n = a + d(n-1) \rightarrow 92 = a + 4(10-1) = a + 36$, now solve for $a$.<br>$92 = a + 36 \rightarrow a = 92 - 36 = 56$,<br>First Five Terms: $56, 60, 64, 68, 72$ |
| **Your Turn!** | **Find the first five terms of the sequences.** |

| **Your Turn!** (continued) | |
|---|---|
| 1) $a_{12} = 122, d = 8$<br><br>$\quad 34, 42, 50, 58, 66$ | 2) $a_{14} = 240, d = 6$<br><br>$\quad 162, 168, 174, 180, 186$ |
| 3) $a_{13} = 216, d = 3$<br><br>$\quad 174, 177, 180, 183, 186$ | 4) $a_{00} = 280, d = 10$<br><br>$\quad 90, 100, 110, 120, 130$ |

| Name: ................................. | Date: ................................. |
|---|---|
| **Topic** | **Geometric Sequences** |

| | |
|---|---|
| **Notes** | ☑ It is a sequence of numbers where each term after the first is found by multiplying the previous item by the common ratio, a fixed, non-zero number. For example, the sequence 2, 4, 8, 16, 32, … is a geometric sequence with common ratio of 2. <br> ☑ To find any term in a geometric sequence use this formula: $x_n = ar^{(n-1)}$, $a$ = the first term, $r$ = the common ratio, $n$ = number of items |
| **Example** | ***Given two terms in a geometric sequence find the 8th term.*** <br> $a_3 = 6$ ***and*** $a_5 = 24$ <br> **Solution:** use geometric sequence formula: $x_n = ar^{(n-1)}$ › $a_3 = ar^{(3-1)} = ar^2 = 6$ <br> $$x_n = ar^{(n-1)} \rightarrow a_5 = ar^{(5-1)} = ar^4 = 24$$ <br> Now divide $a_5$ by $a_3$. Then: $\frac{a_5}{a_3} = \frac{ar^4}{ar^2} = \frac{24}{6} = 4$, Now simplify: $\frac{ar^4}{ar^2} = 4 \rightarrow$ <br> $$r^2 = 4 \rightarrow r = 2$$ <br> We can find $a$ now: $ar^2 = 6 \rightarrow a(2^2) = 6 \rightarrow a = \frac{3}{2}$ <br> Use the formula to find the 8th term: $x_n = ar^{(n-1)} \rightarrow a_8 = \left(\frac{3}{2}\right)(2)^8 = 384$ |
| **Your Turn!** | ***Find the 6th term of each sequences.*** <br><br> 1) $a_2 = 2$ and $a_4 = 18$      2) $a_3 = 20$ and $a_5 = 80$ <br><br> $a_6 =$ ___          $a_6 =$ ___ <br><br> ***Find the first four terms of each sequences.*** <br><br> 3) $a_n = a_{n-1}(6), a_1 = -2$      4) $a_n = a_{n-1}.(4), a_1 = -5$ <br><br> ___, ___, ___, ___       ___, ___, ___, ___ |

| Name: .......................................... | Date: .......................................... |
|---|---|

| **Topic** | **Geometric Sequences** |
|---|---|
| **Notes** | ☑ It is a sequence of numbers where each term after the first is found by multiplying the previous item by the common ratio, a fixed, non-zero number. For example, the sequence 2, 4, 8, 16, 32, … is a geometric sequence with common ratio of 2.<br><br>☑ To find any term in a geometric sequence use this formula: $x_n = ar^{(n-1)}$, $a$ = the first term, $r$ = the common ratio, $n$ = number of items |
| **Example** | **Given two terms in a geometric sequence find the 8th term.**<br>$a_3 = 6$ ***and*** $a_5 = 24$<br>**Solution:** use geometric sequence formula: $x_n = ar^{(n-1)} \rightarrow a_3 = ar^{(3-1)} = ar^2 = 6$<br>$$x_n = ar^{(n-1)} \rightarrow a_5 = ar^{(5-1)} = ar^4 = 24$$<br>Now divide $a_5$ by $a_3$. Then: $\frac{a_5}{a_3} = \frac{ar^4}{ar^2} = \frac{24}{6} = 4$, Now simplify: $\frac{ar^4}{ar^2} = 4 \rightarrow$<br>$$r^2 = 4 \rightarrow r = 2$$<br>We can find $a$ now: $ar^2 = 6 \rightarrow a(2^2) = 6 \rightarrow a = \frac{3}{2}$<br>Use the formula to find the 8th term: $x_n = ar^{(n-1)} \rightarrow a_8 = \left(\frac{3}{2}\right)(2)^8 = 384$ |
| **Your Turn!** | **Find the 6th term of each sequences.**<br><br>1) $a_2 = 2$ and $a_4 = 18$      2) $a_3 = 20$ and $a_5 = 80$<br><br>     $a_6 = 162$                 $a_6 = 320$<br><br>**Find the first four terms of each sequences.**<br><br>3) $a_n = a_{n-1}(6), a_1 = -2$      4) $a_n = a_{n-1}.(4), a_1 = -5$<br><br>    $-2, -12, -72, -432$       $-5, -20, -80, -320$ |

| Name: .............................. | | Date: ................................... |
|---|---|---|

| **Topic** | **Arithmetic Series** | |
|---|---|---|
| **Notes** | ✓ An arithmetic series is the sum of sequence in which each term is computed from the previous one by adding (or subtracting) a constant $d$<br><br>✓ The sum of the sequence of the first $n$ terms is then given by:<br>$S_n = \sum_{k=1}^{n} a_k = \sum_{k=1}^{n} [a_1 + (k-1)d]$<br><br>✓ Using the sum identify $\sum_{k=1}^{n} \frac{1}{2} n(n+1)$ then gives:<br><br>$$S_n = na_1 + \frac{1}{2} dn(n-1) = \frac{1}{2} n[2a_1 + d(n-1)].$$<br><br>✓ Note that:<br><br>$a_1 + a_n = a_1 + [a_1 + d(n-1)] = 2a_1 + d(n-1)$, So: $S_n = \frac{1}{2} n(a_1 + a_n)$ | |
| **Example** | *In the arithmetic series* $3, 6, 9, 12, ...$ *find the sum of the first 8 terms.*<br><br>**Solution:** $a_1 = 3, d = 6 - 3 = 3, n = 8$<br><br>Use arithmetic series formula to find the sum: $S_n = \frac{1}{2} n[2a_1 + d(n-1)]$<br><br>$$S_8 = \frac{8}{2} [2(3) + 3(8-1)] \rightarrow S_8 = 4(6 + 21) = 108$$ | |
| **Your Turn!** | **Evaluate each arithmetic series described.** | |
| | 1) $\sum_{k=1}^{30} 5k - 1$<br><br>$S_{30} = $ ____ | 2) $\sum_{k=1}^{15} 3k + 1$<br><br>$S_{15} = $ ____ |
| | 3) $\sum_{i=1}^{20} 3i - 7$<br><br>$S_{20} = $ ____ | 4) $\sum_{n=1}^{24} 2n - 9$<br><br>$S_{24} = $ ____ |

| Name: .................................. | Date: .................................... |
|---|---|

| Topic | Arithmetic Series |
|---|---|

| | |
|---|---|
| **Notes** | ☑ An arithmetic series is the sum of sequence in which each term is computed from the previous one by adding (or subtracting) a constant $d$.<br><br>☑ The sum of the sequence of the first $n$ terms is then given by:<br>$S_n = \sum_{k=1}^{n} a_k = \sum_{k=1}^{n} [a_1 + (k-1)d]$<br><br>☑ Using the sum identify $\sum_{k=1}^{n} \frac{1}{2} n(n+1)$ then gives:<br><br>$$S_n = na_1 + \frac{1}{2} dn(n-1) = \frac{1}{2} n[2a_1 + d(n-1)].$$<br><br>☑ Note that:<br><br>$$a_1 + a_n = a_1 + [a_1 + d(n-1)] = 2a_1 + d(n-1), \text{ So: } S_n = \frac{1}{2} n(a_1 + a_n)$$ |
| **Example** | ***In the arithmetic series*** $3, 6, 9, 12, \ldots$ ***find the sum of the first 8 terms.***<br><br>**Solution:** $a_1 = 3, d = 6 - 3 = 3, n = 8$<br><br>Use arithmetic series formula to find the sum: $S_n = \frac{1}{2} n[2a_1 + d(n-1)]$<br><br>$$S_8 = \frac{8}{2} [2(3) + 3(8-1)] \rightarrow S_8 = 4(6 + 21) = 108$$ |
| **Your Turn!** | **Evaluate each arithmetic series described.** |

| 1) $\sum_{k=1}^{30} 5k - 1$ <br><br> $S_{30} = 2{,}295$ | 2) $\sum_{k=1}^{15} 3k + 1$ <br><br> $S_{15} = 375$ |
|---|---|
| 3) $\sum_{i=1}^{20} 3i - 7$ <br><br> $S_{20} = 490$ | 4) $\sum_{n=1}^{24} 2n - 9$ <br><br> $S_{24} = 384$ |

| Name: ........................................ | Date: ........................................ |
|---|---|

| Topic | Finite Geometric Series |
|---|---|
| Notes | ✅ The sum of a geometric series is finite when the absolute value of the ratio is less than 1<br>✅ Finite Geometric Series formula:<br>$S_n = \sum_{i=1}^{n} ar^{i-1} = a_1(\frac{1-r^n}{1-r})$ |
| Example | ***Evaluate the geometric series described.***<br>$\sum_{n=1}^{3} 4^{n-1}$<br>***Solution:*** Use this formula: $S_n = \sum_{i=1}^{n} ar^{i-1} = a_1\left(\frac{1-r^n}{1-r}\right) \rightarrow$<br>$\sum_{n=1}^{3} 4^{n-1} = 1\left(\frac{1-4^3}{1-4}\right) \rightarrow 1\left(\frac{1-4^3}{1-4}\right) = 1\left(\frac{1-64}{1-4}\right) = \left(\frac{-63}{-3}\right) = 21$ |
| Your Turn! | **Evaluate each geometric series described.**<br>*1)* $a_1 = 5, r = 2, n = 6$    $S_n =$ ________<br>*2)* $a_1 = -1, r = 5, n = 4$    $S_n =$ ________<br>*3)* $\sum_{m=1}^{5} -4^{m-1}$    $S_n =$ ________<br>*4)* $\sum_{m=1}^{5} (-1).5^{m-1}$    $S_n =$ ________ |

| Name: ....................................... | Date: ...................................... |
|---|---|

| Topic | **Finite Geometric Series** |
|---|---|
| **Notes** | ☑ The sum of a geometric series is finite when the absolute value of the ratio is less than 1.<br><br>☑ Finite Geometric Series formula:<br><br>$$S_n = \sum_{i=1}^{n} ar^{i-1} = a_1\left(\frac{1-r^n}{1-r}\right)$$ |
| **Example** | *Evaluate the geometric series described.*<br><br>$\sum_{n=1}^{3} 4^{n-1}$<br><br>**Solution:** Use this formula: $S_n = \sum_{i=1}^{n} ar^{i-1} = a_1\left(\frac{1-r^n}{1-r}\right) \rightarrow$<br><br>$\sum_{n=1}^{3} 4^{n-1} = 1\left(\frac{1-4^3}{1-4}\right) \rightarrow 1\left(\frac{1-4^3}{1-4}\right) = 1\left(\frac{1-64}{1-4}\right) = \left(\frac{-63}{-3}\right) = 21$ |
| **Your Turn!** | **Evaluate each geometric series described.** |

| 1) $a_1 = 5, r = 2, n = 6$<br><br>$S_n = 315$ | 2) $a_1 = -1, r = 5, n = 4$<br><br>$S_n = -156$ |
|---|---|
| 3) $\sum_{m=1}^{5} -4^{m-1}$<br><br>$S_n = -341$ | 4) $\sum_{m=1}^{5} 5^{m-1}$<br><br>$S_n = 781$ |

| Name: ………………………….. | Date: ………………………….. |

| Topic | Infinite Geometric Series |
|---|---|

| **Notes** | ☑ Infinite Geometric Series:  The sum of a geometric series is infinite when the of the ratio is more than 1. <br><br> ☑ Infinite Geometric Series formula: $S = \sum_{i=0}^{\infty} a_i r^i = \frac{a_1}{1-r}$ |
|---|---|
| **Example** | 1) **Evaluate infinite geometric series described.** $\sum_{i=1}^{\infty} 5^{i-1}$ <br><br> **Solution:** use this formula: $\sum_{i=0}^{\infty} a_i r^i = \frac{a_1}{1-r} \rightarrow \sum_{i=1}^{\infty} 5^{i-1} = \frac{1}{1-5} =$ <br> $\frac{1}{-4} = -\frac{1}{4}$ <br><br> 2) **Evaluate infinite geometric series described.** $\sum_{k=1}^{\infty} (\frac{1}{5})^{k-1}$ <br><br> **Solution:** use this formula: $\sum_{i=0}^{\infty} a_i r^i = \frac{a_1}{1-r} \rightarrow$ <br> $\sum_{k=1}^{\infty} (\frac{1}{5})^{k-1} = \frac{1}{1-\frac{1}{5}} = \frac{1}{\frac{4}{5}} = \frac{5}{4}$ |
| **Your Turn!** | *Evaluate infinite geometric series described.* <br><br> 1) $a_1 = 4, r = \frac{1}{5}$ <br><br> $S = \underline{\hspace{2cm}}$ <br><br> 2) $a_1 = -3, r = \frac{1}{3}$ <br><br> $S = \underline{\hspace{2cm}}$ <br><br> 3) $\sum_{i=1}^{\infty} 6(-\frac{1}{4})^{i-1}$ <br><br> $S = \underline{\hspace{2cm}}$ <br><br> 4) $1 + 0.3 + 0.09 + 0.027 + \cdots$ <br><br> $S = \underline{\hspace{2cm}}$ |

| Name: ................................. | | Date: .................................... |
|---|---|---|
| **Topic** | | **Infinite Geometric Series** |

| **Notes** | ☑ Infinite Geometric Series:  The sum of a geometric series is infinite when the of the ratio is more than 1. <br><br> ☑ Infinite Geometric Series formula:  $S = \sum_{i=0}^{\infty} a_i r^i = \frac{a_1}{1-r}$ |
|---|---|
| **Example** | **3) Evaluate infinite geometric series described.** $\sum_{i=1}^{\infty} 5^{i-1}$ <br><br> **Solution:** use this formula: $\sum_{i=0}^{\infty} a_i r^i = \frac{a_1}{1-r} \rightarrow \sum_{i=1}^{\infty} 5^{i-1} = \frac{1}{1-5} =$ <br> $\frac{1}{-4} = -\frac{1}{4}$ <br><br> **4) Evaluate infinite geometric series described.** $\sum_{k=1}^{\infty} (\frac{1}{5})^{k-1}$ <br><br> **Solution:** use this formula: $\sum_{i=0}^{\infty} a_i r^i = \frac{a_1}{1-r} \rightarrow$ <br> $\sum_{k=1}^{\infty} (\frac{1}{5})^{k-1} = \frac{1}{1-\frac{1}{5}} = \frac{1}{\frac{4}{5}} = \frac{5}{4}$ |

| **Your Turn!** | *Evaluate infinite geometric series described.* | |
|---|---|---|
| | *1)* $a_1 = 4, r = \frac{1}{5}$ <br><br> $S = 5$ | *2)* $a_1 = -3, r = \frac{1}{3}$ <br><br> $S = -\frac{9}{2}$ |
| | *3)* $\sum_{i=1}^{\infty} 6(-\frac{1}{4})^{i-1}$ <br><br> $S = \frac{24}{5}$ | *4)* $1 + 0.3 + 0.09 + 0.027 + \cdots$ <br><br> $S = \frac{10}{7}$ |

# CLEP College Algebra Test Review

College-Level Examination Program (CLEP) is a series of 33 standardized tests that measures your knowledge of certain subjects. You can earn college credit at thousands of colleges and universities by earning a satisfactory score on a computer-based CLEP exam.

The CLEP College Algebra measures your knowledge of math topics generally taught in a one-semester college course in algebra. It contains approximately 60 multiple choice questions to be answered in 90 minutes. Some of these questions are pretest questions that will not be scored. These 60 questions cover: basic algebraic operations; linear and quadratic equations, inequalities, and graphs; algebraic, exponential, and logarithmic functions; and miscellaneous other topics. A scientific calculator is available to students during the entire testing time.

The CLEP College Algebra exam score ranges from 20 to 80 converting to A, B, C, or D based on this score. The letter grade is applied to your college course equivalent.

In this book, there are two complete CLEP College Algebra Tests. Take these tests to see what score you'll be able to receive on a real CLEP College Algebra test.

Good luck!

# Time to Test

## Time to refine your quantitative reasoning skill with a practice test

Take an CLEP College Algebra test to simulate the test day experience. After you've finished, score your test using the answer keys.

## Before You Start

- You'll need a pencil, a calculator and a timer to take the test.

- For most multiple questions, there are five possible answers. Choose which one is best.

- It's okay to guess. There is no penalty for wrong answers.

- Use the answer sheet provided to record your answers.

- **Calculator is permitted for CLEP College Algebra Test.**

- After you've finished the test, review the answer key to see where you went wrong.

**Good Luck!**

# CLEP College Algebra

# Practice Test 1

# 2020 - 2021

**Total number of questions:** 60

**Total time:** 90 Minutes

## Calculator is permitted for CLEP College Algebra Test.

# CLEP College Algebra Practice Test Answer Sheet

Remove (or photocopy) this answer sheet and use it to complete the practice test.

**CLEP College Algebra Practice Test 1 Answer Sheet**

| | | | | | |
|---|---|---|---|---|---|
| 1 | Ⓐ Ⓑ Ⓒ Ⓓ Ⓔ | 21 | Ⓐ Ⓑ Ⓒ Ⓓ Ⓔ | 41 | Ⓐ Ⓑ Ⓒ Ⓓ Ⓔ |
| 2 | Ⓐ Ⓑ Ⓒ Ⓓ Ⓔ | 22 | Ⓐ Ⓑ Ⓒ Ⓓ Ⓔ | 42 | Ⓐ Ⓑ Ⓒ Ⓓ Ⓔ |
| 3 | Ⓐ Ⓑ Ⓒ Ⓓ Ⓔ | 23 | Ⓐ Ⓑ Ⓒ Ⓓ Ⓔ | 43 | Ⓐ Ⓑ Ⓒ Ⓓ Ⓔ |
| 4 | Ⓐ Ⓑ Ⓒ Ⓓ Ⓔ | 24 | Ⓐ Ⓑ Ⓒ Ⓓ Ⓔ | 44 | Ⓐ Ⓑ Ⓒ Ⓓ Ⓔ |
| 5 | Ⓐ Ⓑ Ⓒ Ⓓ Ⓔ | 25 | Ⓐ Ⓑ Ⓒ Ⓓ Ⓔ | 45 | Ⓐ Ⓑ Ⓒ Ⓓ Ⓔ |
| 6 | Ⓐ Ⓑ Ⓒ Ⓓ Ⓔ | 26 | Ⓐ Ⓑ Ⓒ Ⓓ Ⓔ | 46 | Ⓐ Ⓑ Ⓒ Ⓓ Ⓔ |
| 7 | Ⓐ Ⓑ Ⓒ Ⓓ Ⓔ | 27 | Ⓐ Ⓑ Ⓒ Ⓓ Ⓔ | 47 | Ⓐ Ⓑ Ⓒ Ⓓ Ⓔ |
| 8 | Ⓐ Ⓑ Ⓒ Ⓓ Ⓔ | 28 | Ⓐ Ⓑ Ⓒ Ⓓ Ⓔ | 48 | Ⓐ Ⓑ Ⓒ Ⓓ Ⓔ |
| 9 | Ⓐ Ⓑ Ⓒ Ⓓ Ⓔ | 29 | Ⓐ Ⓑ Ⓒ Ⓓ Ⓔ | 49 | Ⓐ Ⓑ Ⓒ Ⓓ Ⓔ |
| 10 | Ⓐ Ⓑ Ⓒ Ⓓ Ⓔ | 30 | Ⓐ Ⓑ Ⓒ Ⓓ Ⓔ | 50 | Ⓐ Ⓑ Ⓒ Ⓓ Ⓔ |
| 11 | Ⓐ Ⓑ Ⓒ Ⓓ Ⓔ | 31 | Ⓐ Ⓑ Ⓒ Ⓓ Ⓔ | 51 | Ⓐ Ⓑ Ⓒ Ⓓ Ⓔ |
| 12 | Ⓐ Ⓑ Ⓒ Ⓓ Ⓔ | 32 | Ⓐ Ⓑ Ⓒ Ⓓ Ⓔ | 52 | Ⓐ Ⓑ Ⓒ Ⓓ Ⓔ |
| 13 | Ⓐ Ⓑ Ⓒ Ⓓ Ⓔ | 33 | Ⓐ Ⓑ Ⓒ Ⓓ Ⓔ | 53 | Ⓐ Ⓑ Ⓒ Ⓓ Ⓔ |
| 14 | Ⓐ Ⓑ Ⓒ Ⓓ Ⓔ | 34 | Ⓐ Ⓑ Ⓒ Ⓓ Ⓔ | 54 | Ⓐ Ⓑ Ⓒ Ⓓ Ⓔ |
| 15 | Ⓐ Ⓑ Ⓒ Ⓓ Ⓔ | 35 | Ⓐ Ⓑ Ⓒ Ⓓ Ⓔ | 55 | Ⓐ Ⓑ Ⓒ Ⓓ Ⓔ |
| 16 | Ⓐ Ⓑ Ⓒ Ⓓ Ⓔ | 36 | Ⓐ Ⓑ Ⓒ Ⓓ Ⓔ | 56 | Ⓐ Ⓑ Ⓒ Ⓓ Ⓔ |
| 17 | Ⓐ Ⓑ Ⓒ Ⓓ Ⓔ | 37 | Ⓐ Ⓑ Ⓒ Ⓓ Ⓔ | 57 | Ⓐ Ⓑ Ⓒ Ⓓ Ⓔ |
| 18 | Ⓐ Ⓑ Ⓒ Ⓓ Ⓔ | 38 | Ⓐ Ⓑ Ⓒ Ⓓ Ⓔ | 58 | Ⓐ Ⓑ Ⓒ Ⓓ Ⓔ |
| 19 | Ⓐ Ⓑ Ⓒ Ⓓ Ⓔ | 39 | Ⓐ Ⓑ Ⓒ Ⓓ Ⓔ | 59 | Ⓐ Ⓑ Ⓒ Ⓓ Ⓔ |
| 20 | Ⓐ Ⓑ Ⓒ Ⓓ Ⓔ | 40 | Ⓐ Ⓑ Ⓒ Ⓓ Ⓔ | 60 | Ⓐ Ⓑ Ⓒ Ⓓ Ⓔ |

1) If $f(x) = 2x + 2$ and $g(x) = x^2 + 4x$, then find $\left(\frac{f}{g}\right)(x)$.

A. $\dfrac{2x+2}{x^2+4x}$

B. $\dfrac{x+1}{x^2+2x}$

C. $\dfrac{2x+2}{x^2+x}$

D. $\dfrac{\;\;\;\;}{x^2+x}$

E. $\dfrac{x^2+4x}{2x+2}$

2) In the standard $(x, y)$ coordinate plane, which of the following lines contains the points (3, −5) and (8, 15)?

A. $y = 4x - 17$

B. $y = \frac{1}{4}x + 13$

C. $y = -4x + 7$

D. $y = -\frac{1}{4}x + 17$

E. $y = 2x - 11$

3) Which of the following is equal to the expression below?

$$(5x + 2y)(2x - y)$$

A. $4x^2 - 2y^2$

B. $2x^2 + 6xy - 2y^2$

C. $24x^2 + 2xy - 2y^2$

D. $10x^2 - xy - 2y^2$

E. $8x^2 + 2xy - 2y^2$

4) What is the product of all possible values of $x$ in the following equation? $|x - 10| = 4$

A. 3

B. 7

C. 13

D. 84

E. 100

5) What is the slope of a line that is perpendicular to the line $4x - 2y = 6$?

A. $-2$

B. $-\frac{1}{2}$

C. 4

D. 12

E. 14

6) What is the value of the expression $6(x - 2y) + (2 - x)^2$ when $x = 3$ and $= -2$ ?

A. $-4$

B. 20

C. 43

D. 50

E. 80

7) For $i = \sqrt{-1}$, which of the following is equivalent of $\frac{2+3i}{5-2i}$ ?

A. $\frac{3+2i}{5}$

B. 5+3i

C. $\frac{4+19i}{29}$

D. $\frac{4+19i}{20}$

E. $\frac{4+21i}{20}$

8) If function is defined as $f(x) = bx^2 + 15$, and $b$ is a constant and $f(2) = 35$. What is the value of $f(3)$?

A. 25

B. 35

C. 60

D. 65

E. 75

9) What is the area of a square whose diagonal is 4?

A. 4

B. 8

C. 16

D. 64

E. 124

10) The average of five numbers is 26. If a sixth number 42 is added, then, what is the new average? (round your answer to the nearest hundredth)

A. 25

B. 26.5

C. 27

D. 28.66

E. 36

11) A construction company is building a wall. The company can build 30 cm of the wall per minute. After 40 minutes $\frac{3}{4}$ of the wall is completed. How many meters is the wall?

A. 6

B. 8

C. 14

D. 16

E. 20

12) What is the solution of the following inequality?

$$|x - 2| \geq 3$$

A. $x \geq 5 \cup x \leq -1$

B. $-1 \leq x \leq 5$

C. $x \geq 5$

D. $x \leq -1$

E. Set of real numbers

13) When 5 times the number $x$ is added to 10, the result is 35. What is the result when 3 times $x$ is added to 6?

A. 10

B. 15

C. 21

D. 25

E. 28

14) If $3h + g = 8h + 4$, what is $g$ in terms of $h$?

A. $h = 5g - 4$

B. $g = 5h + 4$

C. $h = 4g$

D. $g = h + 1$

E. $g = 5h + 1$

15) What is the value of $x$ in the following equation? $\frac{2}{3}x + \frac{1}{6} = \frac{1}{2}$

A. 6

B. $\frac{1}{2}$

C. $\frac{1}{3}$

D. $\frac{1}{4}$

E. $\frac{1}{12}$

16) A bank is offering 4.5% simple interest on a savings account. If you deposit $12,000, how much interest will you earn in two years?

A. $420

B. $1,080

C. $4,200

D. $8,400

E. $9,600

17) Simplify $7x^2y^3(2x^2y)^3 =$

A. $12x^4y^6$

B. $12x^8y^6$

C. $56x^4y^6$

D. $56x^8y^6$

E. $96x^8y^6$

18) What are the zeroes of the function $f(x) = x^3 + 7x^2 + 12x$?

**A. 0**

B. $-4, -3$

**C. 0, 2, 3**

D. $-3, -5$

**E. 0, $-3, -4$**

19) If $x + sin^2a + cos^2a = 3$, then $x = $?

A. 1

B. 2

C. 3

D. 4

E. 5

20) If $\sqrt{3x} = \sqrt{y}$, then $x =$

A. $3y$

B. $\sqrt{\dfrac{y}{3}}$

C. $\sqrt{3y}$

D. $y^2$

E. $\dfrac{y}{3}$

21) If $f(x)=2x^3 + 5x^2 + 2x$ and $g(x)= -4$, what is the value of $f(g(x))$?

A. 56

B. 32

C. 24

D. $-4$

E. $-56$

22) A cruise line ship left Port A and traveled 50 miles due west and then 120 miles due north. At this point, what is the shortest distance from the cruise to port A?

A. 70 *miles*

B. 80 *miles*

C. 150 *miles*

D. 230 *miles*

E. 130 *miles*

23) What is the equivalent temperature of 104°*F* in Celsius?

$$C = \frac{5}{9}(F - 32)$$

A. 32

B. 40

C. 48

D. 52

E. 64

24) The perimeter of a rectangular yard is 72 meters. What is its length if its width is twice its length?

A. 12 *meters*

B. 18 *meters*

C. 20 *meters*

D. 24 *meters*

E. 36 *meters*

25) The average of 6 numbers is 14. The average of 4 of those numbers is 10. What is the average of the other two numbers?

A. 10

B. 12

C. 14

D. 22

E. 24

26) If 150% of a number is 75, then what is the 80% of that number?

A. 40

B. 50

C. 70

D. 85

F 90

27) What is the slope of the line: $4x - 2y = 12$

A. $-1$

B. $-2$

C. 1

D. 1.5

E. 2

28) In two successive years, the population of a town is increased by 10% and 20%. What percent of the population is increased after two years?

A. 30%

B. 32%

C. 35%

D. 68%

E. 70%

29) The area of a circle is $36\pi$. What is the diameter of the circle?

A. 4

B. 8

C. 12

D. 14

E. 16

30) If 20% of a number is 4, what is the number?

A. 4

B. 8

C. 10

D. 20

E. 25

31) What is the value of $x$ in the following system of equations?

$$5x + 2y = 3$$

$$y = x$$

A. $x = \dfrac{3}{7}$

B. $x = \dfrac{1}{3}$

C. $x = \dfrac{2}{3}$

D. $x = \dfrac{4}{3}$

E. $x = \dfrac{5}{3}$

32) In a hotel, there are 5 floors and $x$ rooms on each floor. If each room has exactly $y$ chairs, which of the following gives the total number of chairs in the hotel?

A. $5xy$

B. $2xy$

C. $x + y$

D. $x + 5y$

E. $2x + 5y$

33) If $\alpha = 2\beta$ and $\beta = 3\gamma$, how many $\alpha$ are equal to $36\gamma$?

A. 12

B. 2

C. 6

D. 4

E. 1

34) If $f(x) = 2x^3 + 5x^2 + 2x$ and $g(x) = -3$, what is the value of $f(g(x))$?

A. 36

B. 32

C. 24

D. 15

E. $-15$

35) The diagonal of a rectangle is 10 inches long and the height of the rectangle is 6 inches. What is the perimeter of the rectangle?

A. 10 *inches*

B. 12 *inches*

C. 16 *inches*

D. 18 *inches*

E. 28 *inches*

36) The perimeter of the trapezoid below is 40 *cm*. What is its area?

A. 48 $cm^2$

B. 98 $cm^2$

C. 140 $cm^2$

D. 576 $cm^2$

E. 986 $cm^2$

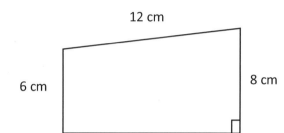

37) If $f(x)=2x^3+2$ and $g(x)=\frac{1}{x}$, what is the value of $f(g(x))$?

A. $\dfrac{1}{2x^3+2}$

B. $\dfrac{2}{x^3}$

C. $\dfrac{1}{2x}$

D. $\dfrac{1}{2x+2}$

E. $\dfrac{2}{x^3}+2$

38) A cruise line ship left Port $A$ and traveled 80 miles due west and then 150 miles due north. At this point, what is the shortest distance from the cruise to port $A$?

A. 70 miles

B. 80 miles

C. 150 miles

D. 170 miles

E. 230 miles

39) If the ratio of $5a$ to $2b$ is $\frac{1}{10}$, what is the ratio of $a$ to $b$?

A. 10

B. 25

C. $\frac{1}{25}$

D. $\frac{1}{20}$

E. $\frac{1}{10}$

40) If $x = 9$, what is the value of $y$ in the following equation? $2y = \frac{2x^2}{3} + 6$

A. 30

B. 45

C. 60

D. 120

E. 180

41) If $\frac{x-3}{5} = N$ and $N = 6$, what is the value of $x$?

A. 25

B. 28

C. 30

D. 33

E. 36

42) Which of the following is equal to $b^{\frac{3}{5}}$?

A. $\sqrt{b^{\frac{5}{3}}}$

B. $b^{\frac{5}{3}}$

C. $\sqrt[5]{b^3}$

D. $\sqrt[3]{b^5}$

E. $\sqrt[3]{b^{-5}}$

43) On Saturday, Sara read $N$ pages of a book each hour for 3 hours, and Mary read $M$ pages of a book each hour for 4 hours. Which of the following represents the total number of pages of book read by Sara and Mary on Saturday?

A. $12MN$

B. $3N + 4M$

C. $7MN$

D. $4N + 3M$

E. $4N - 3M$

44) Simplify $(-4 + 9i)(3 + 5i)$.

A. $54 - 7i$

B. $-54 + 7i$

C. $-57 + 7i$

D. $57 - 7i$

E. $-57 - 7i$

45) If function is defined as $f(x) = bx^2 + 15$, and $b$ is a constant and $f(2) = 35$. What is the value of $f(5)$?

A. $25$

B. $35$

C. $140$

D. $165$

E. $168$

46) Find the solution $(x, y)$ to the following system of equations?
$$2x + 5y = 11$$
$$4x - 2y = -14$$

A. $(14, 5)$

B. $(6, 8)$

C. $(11, 17)$

D. $(-2, 3)$

E. $(2, 3)$

47) Calculate $f(4)$ for the function $f(x) = 3x^2 - 4$.

A. 44

B. 40

C. 38

D. 30

E. 20

48) What are the zeroes of the function $f(x) = x^3 + 5x^2 + 6x$?

A. 0

B. 2

C. $0, 2, 3$

D. $0, -2, -3$

E. $0, -2, 3$

49) Simplify $\frac{4-3i}{-4i}$?

A. $i$

B. $\frac{3i}{4}$

C. $\frac{3}{4} - i$

D. $\frac{3}{4} + i$

E. $4 + i$

$$y = x^2 - 7x + 12$$

50) The equation above represents a parabola in the $xy$-plane. Which of the following equivalent forms of the equation displays the $x$-intercepts of the parabola as constants or coefficients?

A. $y = x + 3$

B. $y = x(x - 7)$

C. $y = (x + 3)(x + 4)$

D. $y = (x - 3)(x - 4)$

E. $y = (x - 4)(x - 7)$

51) The function $g(x)$ is defined by a polynomial. Some values of $x$ and $g(x)$ are shown in the table below. Which of the following must be a factor of $g(x)$?

| $x$ | $g(x)$ |
|-----|--------|
| 0 | 5 |
| 1 | 4 |
| 2 | 0 |

A. $x$

B. $x - 1$

C. $x - 2$

D. $x + 1$

E. $x + 6$

52) What is the value of $\frac{4b}{c}$ when $\frac{c}{b} = 2$

A. 8

B. 4

C. 2

D. 1

E. 0

53) If $x + 5 = 8$, $2y - 1 = 5$ then $xy + 15 =$

A. 30

B. 24

C. 21

D. 17

E. 15

54) If $\frac{a-b}{b} = \frac{10}{13}$, then which of the following must be true?

A. $\frac{a}{b} = \frac{10}{13}$

B. $\frac{a}{b} = \frac{23}{13}$

C. $\frac{a}{b} = \frac{13}{21}$

D. $\frac{a}{b} = \frac{21}{10}$

E. $\frac{a}{b} = \frac{10}{23}$

55) Which of the following lines is parallel to: $6y - 2x = 24$?

A. $y = \frac{1}{3}x + 2$

B. $y = 3x + 5$

C. $y = x - 2$

D. $y = 2x - 1$

E. $y = -x - 1$

56) The average of $13, 15, 20$ and $x$ is $20$. What is the value of $x$

A. 9

B. 15

C. 18

D. 32

E. 36

57) Solve the following equation for $y$?

$$\frac{x}{7} = \frac{y}{3}$$

A. $\frac{3}{5}x$

B. $\frac{3}{7}x$

C. $3x$

D. $x$

E. $-x$

58) If the interior angles of a quadrilateral are in the ratio $1:2:3:4$, what is the measure of the smallest angle?

A. $36°$

B. $72°$

C. $108°$

D. $144°$

E. $154°$

59) Sara orders a box of pen for $3 per box. A tax of 8.5% is added to the cost of the pens before a flat shipping fee of $6 closest out the transaction. Which of the following represents total cost of $p$ boxes of pens in dollars?

A. $1.085(3p) + 6$

B. $6p + 3$

C. $1.085(6p) + 3$

D. $3p + 6$

E. $6p + 6$

60) A plant grows at a linear rate. After five weeks, the plant is $40\ cm$ tall. Which of the following functions represents the relationship between the height $(y)$ of the plant and number of weeks of growth $(x)$?

A. $y(x) = 40x + 8$

B. $y(x) = 8x + 40$

C. $y(x) = 40x$

D. $y(x) = 8x$

E. $y(x) = 4x$

## End of CLEP College Algebra Practice Test 1

# CLEP College Algebra

## Practice Test 2

# 2020 - 2021

**Total number of questions:** 60

**Total time:** 90 Minutes

## Calculator is permitted for CLEP College Algebra Test.

# CLEP College Algebra Practice Test Answer Sheet

**Remove (or photocopy) this answer sheet and use it to complete the practice test.**

CLEP College Algebra Practice Test 2 Answer Sheet

| 1 | Ⓐ Ⓑ Ⓒ Ⓓ Ⓔ | 21 | Ⓐ Ⓑ Ⓒ Ⓓ Ⓔ | 41 | Ⓐ Ⓑ Ⓒ Ⓓ Ⓔ |
|---|---|---|---|---|---|
| 2 | Ⓐ Ⓑ Ⓒ Ⓓ Ⓔ | 22 | Ⓐ Ⓑ Ⓒ Ⓓ Ⓔ | 42 | Ⓐ Ⓑ Ⓒ Ⓓ Ⓔ |
| 3 | Ⓐ Ⓑ Ⓒ Ⓓ Ⓔ | 23 | Ⓐ Ⓑ Ⓒ Ⓓ Ⓔ | 43 | Ⓐ Ⓑ Ⓒ Ⓓ Ⓔ |
| 4 | Ⓐ Ⓑ Ⓒ Ⓓ Ⓔ | 24 | Ⓐ Ⓑ Ⓒ Ⓓ Ⓔ | 44 | Ⓐ Ⓑ Ⓒ Ⓓ Ⓔ |
| 5 | Ⓐ Ⓑ Ⓒ Ⓓ Ⓔ | 25 | Ⓐ Ⓑ Ⓒ Ⓓ Ⓔ | 45 | Ⓐ Ⓑ Ⓒ Ⓓ Ⓔ |
| 6 | Ⓐ Ⓑ Ⓒ Ⓓ Ⓔ | 26 | Ⓐ Ⓑ Ⓒ Ⓓ Ⓔ | 46 | Ⓐ Ⓑ Ⓒ Ⓓ Ⓔ |
| 7 | Ⓐ Ⓑ Ⓒ Ⓓ Ⓔ | 27 | Ⓐ Ⓑ Ⓒ Ⓓ Ⓔ | 47 | Ⓐ Ⓑ Ⓒ Ⓓ Ⓔ |
| 8 | Ⓐ Ⓑ Ⓒ Ⓓ Ⓔ | 28 | Ⓐ Ⓑ Ⓒ Ⓓ Ⓔ | 48 | Ⓐ Ⓑ Ⓒ Ⓓ Ⓔ |
| 9 | Ⓐ Ⓑ Ⓒ Ⓓ Ⓔ | 29 | Ⓐ Ⓑ Ⓒ Ⓓ Ⓔ | 49 | Ⓐ Ⓑ Ⓒ Ⓓ Ⓔ |
| 10 | Ⓐ Ⓑ Ⓒ Ⓓ Ⓔ | 30 | Ⓐ Ⓑ Ⓒ Ⓓ Ⓔ | 50 | Ⓐ Ⓑ Ⓒ Ⓓ Ⓔ |
| 11 | Ⓐ Ⓑ Ⓒ Ⓓ Ⓔ | 31 | Ⓐ Ⓑ Ⓒ Ⓓ Ⓔ | 51 | Ⓐ Ⓑ Ⓒ Ⓓ Ⓔ |
| 12 | Ⓐ Ⓑ Ⓒ Ⓓ Ⓔ | 32 | Ⓐ Ⓑ Ⓒ Ⓓ Ⓔ | 52 | Ⓐ Ⓑ Ⓒ Ⓓ Ⓔ |
| 13 | Ⓐ Ⓑ Ⓒ Ⓓ Ⓔ | 33 | Ⓐ Ⓑ Ⓒ Ⓓ Ⓔ | 53 | Ⓐ Ⓑ Ⓒ Ⓓ Ⓔ |
| 14 | Ⓐ Ⓑ Ⓒ Ⓓ Ⓔ | 34 | Ⓐ Ⓑ Ⓒ Ⓓ Ⓔ | 54 | Ⓐ Ⓑ Ⓒ Ⓓ Ⓔ |
| 15 | Ⓐ Ⓑ Ⓒ Ⓓ Ⓔ | 35 | Ⓐ Ⓑ Ⓒ Ⓓ Ⓔ | 55 | Ⓐ Ⓑ Ⓒ Ⓓ Ⓔ |
| 16 | Ⓐ Ⓑ Ⓒ Ⓓ Ⓔ | 36 | Ⓐ Ⓑ Ⓒ Ⓓ Ⓔ | 56 | Ⓐ Ⓑ Ⓒ Ⓓ Ⓔ |
| 17 | Ⓐ Ⓑ Ⓒ Ⓓ Ⓔ | 37 | Ⓐ Ⓑ Ⓒ Ⓓ Ⓔ | 57 | Ⓐ Ⓑ Ⓒ Ⓓ Ⓔ |
| 18 | Ⓐ Ⓑ Ⓒ Ⓓ Ⓔ | 38 | Ⓐ Ⓑ Ⓒ Ⓓ Ⓔ | 58 | Ⓐ Ⓑ Ⓒ Ⓓ Ⓔ |
| 19 | Ⓐ Ⓑ Ⓒ Ⓓ Ⓔ | 39 | Ⓐ Ⓑ Ⓒ Ⓓ Ⓔ | 59 | Ⓐ Ⓑ Ⓒ Ⓓ Ⓔ |
| 20 | Ⓐ Ⓑ Ⓒ Ⓓ Ⓔ | 40 | Ⓐ Ⓑ Ⓒ Ⓓ Ⓔ | 60 | Ⓐ Ⓑ Ⓒ Ⓓ Ⓔ |

1) When a number is subtracted from 24 and the difference is divided by that number, the result is 3. What is the value of the number?

A. 2

B. 4

C. 6

D. 12

E. 24

2) An angle is equal to one fifth of its supplement. What is the measure of that angle?

A. 20

B. 30

C. 45

D. 60

E. 90

3) Which of the following is one solution of this equation?

$$x^2 + 2x - 5 = 0$$

A. $\sqrt{6} - 1$

B. $\sqrt{2} + 1$

C. $\sqrt{6} + 1$

D. $\sqrt{2} - 1$

E. $\sqrt{12}$

4) Simplify $\frac{4-3i}{-4i}$ ?

A. $\frac{3}{4} + i$

B. $\frac{3}{4} - i$

C. $\frac{1}{4} - i$

D. $\frac{1}{4} + i$

E. $i$

$$4x^2 + 6x - 3 \ , \ 3x^2 - 5x + 8$$

5) Which of the following is the sum of the two polynomials shown above?

A. $5x^2 + 3x + 4$

B. $4x^2 - 6x + 3$

C. $7x^2 + x + 5$

D. $7x^2 + 5x + 1$

E. $x^2 + 5x + 4$

| $x$ | 1 | 2 | 3 |
|---|---|---|---|
| $g(x)$ | $-1$ | $-3$ | $-5$ |

6) The table above shows some values of linear function $g(x)$. Which of the following defines $g(x)$?

A. $g(x) = 2x + 1$

B. $g(x) = 2x - 1$

C. $g(x) = -2x + 1$

D. $g(x) = x + 2$

E. $g(x) = 2x + 2$

7) Right triangle $ABC$ has two legs of lengths $6\ cm\ (AB)$ and $8\ cm\ (AC)$. What is the length of the third side $(BC)$?

A. $4\ cm$

B. $6\ cm$

C. $8\ cm$

D. $10\ cm$

E. $20\ cm$

8) Which of the following expressions is equal to $\sqrt{\dfrac{x^2}{2} + \dfrac{x^2}{16}}$?

A. $x$

B. $\dfrac{3x}{4}$

C. $x\sqrt{x}$

D. $\dfrac{x\sqrt{x}}{4}$

E. $4x$

9) What is the $y$ −intercept of the line with the equation $x - 3y = 12$?

A. 1

B. −2

C. 3

D. −4

E. 5

10) If $4a - 3 = 14$ what is the value of $6a$?

A. 5

B. 15

C. 30

D. 45

E. 50

11) Two third of 18 is equal to $\frac{2}{5}$ of what number?

A. 12

B. 20

C. 30

D. 60

E. 90

12) The marked price of a computer is $D$ dollar. Its price decreased by 20% in January and later increased by 10% in February. What is the final price of the computer in $D$ dollar?

A. 0.80 $D$

B. 0.88 $D$

C. 0.90 $D$

D. 1.20 $D$

E. 1.40 $D$

13) If $x \neq 0$ and $x = x^{-6}$, what is the value of $x$?

A. $-2$

B. $1$

C. $2$

D. $3$

E. $4$

14) Which of the following is equal to expression $\frac{5}{x^2} + \frac{7x-3}{x^3}$ ?

A. $\frac{6x+1}{x^3}$

B. $\frac{10x+6}{x^3}$

C. $\frac{12x+1}{x^3}$

D. $\frac{13x+2}{x^3}$

E. $\frac{6x+4}{x^3}$

15) Which of the following is the equation of a quadratic graph with a vertex $(3, -3)$?

A. $y = 3x^2 - 3$

B. $y = -3x^2 + 3$

C. $y = x^2 + 3x - 3$

D. $y = 4(x - 3)^2 - 3$

E. $y = 4x^2 + 3x - 3$

16) A boat sails 40 miles south and then 30 miles east. How far is the boat from its start point?

A. $45\ miles$

B. $50\ miles$

C. $60\ miles$

D. $70\ miles$

E. $80\ miles$

17) What is the average of $4x + 2, -6x - 5$ and $8x + 2$?

A. $3x + 2$

B. $3x - 2$

C. $2x + 1$

D. $2x - \frac{1}{3}$

E. $x - \frac{1}{3}$

18) The score of Emma was half as that of Ava and the score of Mia was twice that of Ava. If the score of Mia was 60, what is the score of Emma?

A. 12

B. 15

C. 20

D. 30

E. 40

19) The average of five consecutive numbers is 38. What is the smallest number?

A. 38

B. 36

C. 34

D. 12

E. 8

20) Tickets to a movie cost $12.50 for adults and $7.50 for students. A group of 12 friends purchased tickets for $125. How many student tickets did they buy?

A. 3

B. 5

C. 7

D. 8

E. 9

21) If the ratio of $5a$ to $2b$ is $\frac{1}{10}$, what is the ratio of $a$ to $b$?

A. 10

B. 25

C. $\frac{1}{25}$

D. $\frac{1}{20}$

E. $\frac{1}{10}$

22) A chemical solution contains 4% alcohol. If there is $24\ ml$ of alcohol, what is the volume of the solution?

A. $240\ ml$

B. $480\ ml$

C. $600\ ml$

D. $1,200\ ml$

E. $2,400\ ml$

23) The average weight of 18 girls in a class is $60\ kg$ and the average weight of 32 boys in the same class is $62\ kg$. What is the average weight of all the 50 students in that class?

A. 60

B. 61.28

C. 61.68

D. 61.90

E. 62.20

24) If $x = 9$, what is the value of $y$ in the following equation? $2y = \frac{2x^2}{3} + 6$

A. 30

B. 45

C. 60

D. 120

E. 180

25) Sara orders a box of pen for $3 per box. A tax of 8.5% is added to the cost of the pens before a flat shipping fee of $6 closest out the transaction. Which of the following represents total cost of $p$ boxes of pens in dollars?

A. $1.085(3p) + 6$

B. $6p + 3$

C. $1.085(6p) + 3$

D. $3p + 6$

E. $p + 6$

26) The average of $13, 15, 20$ and $x$ is $18$. What is the value of $x$?

A. 9

B. 15

C. 18

D. 20

E. 24

27) The price of a sofa is decreased by 25% to $420. What was its original price?

A. $480

B. $520

C. $560

D. $600

E. $800

28) A bank is offering 4.5% simple interest on a savings account. If you deposit $8,000, how much interest will you earn in five years?

A. $360

B. $720

C. $1,800

D. $3,600

E. $4,800

29) Multiply and write the product in scientific notation: $(4.2 \times 10^6) \times (2.6 \times 10^{-5})$

A. $1092 \times 10$

B. $10.92 \times 10^6$

C. $109.2 \times 10^{-5}$

D. $10.92 \times 10^{11}$

E. $1.092 \times 10^2$

30) A plant grows at a linear rate. After 3 weeks, the plant is 45 cm tall. Which of the following functions represents the relationship between the height $(y)$ of the plant and number of weeks of growth $(x)$?

A. $y(x) = 40x + 8$

B. $y(x) = 25x + 40$

C. $y(x) = 20x$

D. $y(x) = 15x$

E. $y(x) = 3x$

31) Solve for $x$: $4(x + 1) = 6(x - 4) + 20$

A. 12

B. 8

C. 6.2

D. 5.5

E. 4

32) Which of the following expressions is equivalent to $2x\,(4 + 2y)$?

A. $2xy + 8x$

B. $8xy + 8x$

C. $xy + 8$

D. $2xy + 8x$

E. $4xy + 8x$

33) If $y = 4ab + 3b^3$, what is y when $a = 2$ and $b = 3$?

A. 24

B. 31

C. 36

D. 51

E. 105

34) If $x \begin{bmatrix} 2 & 0 \\ 0 & 4 \end{bmatrix} = \begin{bmatrix} x + 3y - 5 & 0 \\ 0 & 2y + 10 \end{bmatrix}$, what is the product of $x$ and $y$?

A. 1

B. 2

C. 10

D. 11

E. 12

35) If $f(x) = 3^x$ and $g(x) = log_3 x$, which of the following expressions is equal to $f(3g(p))$?

A. $3P$

B. $3^p$

C. $p^3$

D. $p^9$

E. $\frac{p}{3}$

36) The following table represents the value of $x$ and function $f(x)$. Which of the following could be the equation of the function $f(x)$?

A. $f(x) = x^2 - 5$

B. $f(x) = x^2 - 1$

C. $f(x) = \sqrt{x + 2}$

D. $f(x) = \sqrt{x} + 4$

E. $f(x) = \sqrt{x} + 6$

| $x$ | $f(x)$ |
|-----|--------|
| 1 | 5 |
| 4 | 6 |
| 9 | 7 |
| 16 | 8 |

37) Which of the following points lies on the line $2x + 4y = 10$

A. $(2, 1)$

B. $(-1, 3)$

C. $(-2, 2)$

D. $(2, 2)$

E. $(2, 0)$

38) Which graph shows a non-proportional linear relationship between $x$ and $y$?

□ A.

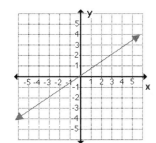

□ B.

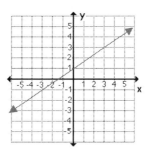

□ C.

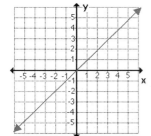

□ D.

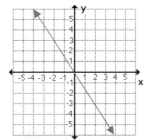

39) A ladder leans against a wall forming a $60°$ angle between the ground and the ladder. If the bottom of the ladder is 30 feet away from the wall, how long is the ladder?

A. $30\ feet$

B. $40\ feet$

C. $50\ feet$

D. $60\ feet$

E. $120\ feet$

40) Right triangle $ABC$ is shown below. Which of the following is true for all possible values of angle $A$ and $B$?

A. $tan\ A\ =\ tan\ B$

B. $sin\ A\ =\ cos\ B$

C. $tan^2 A = tan^2 B$

D. $tan\ A = 1$

E. $cot\ A = sin B$

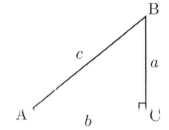

41) If $x + y = 0, 4x - 2y = 24$, which of the following ordered pairs $(x, y)$ satisfies both equations?

A. $(4, 3)$

B. $(5, 4)$

C. $(4, -4)$

D. $(4, -6)$

E. $(2, -6)$

42) If $f(x) = 3x + 4(x + 1) + 2$ then $f(3x) =?$

A. $21x + 6$

B. $16x - 6$

C. $25x + 4$

D. $12x + 3$

E. $2x + 3$

43) A line in the $xy$-plane passes through origin and has a slope of $\frac{2}{3}$. Which of the following points lies on the line?

A. $(2,1)$

B. $(4,1)$

C. $(9,6)$

D. $(9,3)$

E. $(6, -3)$

44) Which of the following is equivalent to $(3n^2 + 4n + 6) - (2n^2 - 5)$?

A. $n + 4n^2$

B. $n^2 - 3$

C. $n^2 + 4n + 11$

D. $n + 2$

E. $n - 2$

45) If $(ax + 4)(bx + 3) = 10x^2 + cx + 12$ for all values of $x$ and $a + b = 7$, what are the two possible values for $c$?

A. $22, 21$

B. $20, 22$

C. $23, 26$

D. $24, 23$

E. $24, 26$

46) If $x \neq -4$ and $x \neq 6$, which of the following is equivalent to $\dfrac{1}{\frac{1}{x-6} + \frac{1}{x+4}}$?

A. $\dfrac{(x-6)(x+4)}{(x-6)+(x+4)}$

B. $\dfrac{(x+4)+(x-6)}{(x+4)(x-6)}$

C. $\dfrac{(x+4)(x-6)}{(x+4)-(x+6)}$

D. $\dfrac{(x+4)+(x-6)}{(x+4)-(x-6)}$

E. $\dfrac{(x-4)+(x-6)}{(x+4)-(x-6)}$

$$y < a - x \ , \ y > x + b$$

47) In the $xy$-plane, if $(0, 0)$ is a solution to the system of inequalities above, which of the following relationships between $a$ and $b$ must be true?

A. $a < b$

B. $a > b$

C. $a = b$

D. $a = b + a$

E. $a = b - a$

48) Which of the following points lies on the line that goes through the points $(2, 4)$ and $(4, 5)$?

A. $(9, 9)$

B. $(9, 6)$

C. $(6, 9)$

D. $(6, 6)$

E. $(0, 0)$

49) Calculate $f(4)$ for the following function $f$.

$$f(x) = x^2 - 3x$$

A. $0$

B. $4$

C. $12$

D. $20$

E. $24$

50) John buys a pepper plant that is 6 inches tall. With regular watering the plant grows 4 inches a year. Writing John's plant's height as a function of time, what does the $y$ −intercept represent?

A. The $y$ −intercept represents the rate of grows of the plant which is 4 inches

B. The $y$ −intercept represents the starting height of 6 inches

C. The $y$ −intercept represents the rate of growth of plant which is 4 inches per year

D. The $y$ −intercept is zero

E. There is no $y$ −intercept

51) If $\dfrac{3}{x} = \dfrac{12}{x-9}$ what is the value of $\dfrac{x}{6}$?

A. $-2$

B. $2$

C. $-\dfrac{1}{2}$

D. $\dfrac{1}{2}$

E. $0$

52) Which of the following is an equation of a circle in the $xy$-plane with center $(0, 4)$ and a radius with endpoint $(\frac{5}{3}, 6)$?

A. $(x + 1)^2 + (y - 4)^2 = \frac{61}{9}$

B. $2x^2 + (y + 4)^2 = \frac{61}{9}$

C. $(x - 2)^2 + (y - 4)^2 = \frac{61}{9}$

D. $x^2 + (y - 4)^2 = \frac{61}{9}$

E. $x^2 + (y - 4)^2 = 25$

53) Given a right triangle $\triangle ABC$ whose $n\angle B = 90°$, $\sin C = \frac{2}{3}$, find $\cos A$?

A. $1$

B. $\frac{1}{2}$

C. $\frac{2}{3}$

D. $\frac{3}{2}$

E. $\frac{5}{2}$

54) What is the equation of the following graph?

A. $x^2 + 6x + 5$

B. $x^2 + 2x + 4$

C. $2x^2 - 4x + 4$

D. $2x^2 + 4x + 2$

E. $4x^2 + 2x + 3$

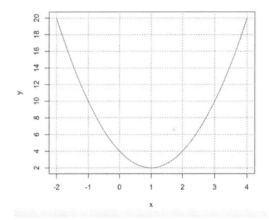

55) In the $xy-$plane, the line determined by the points $(6, m)$ and $(m, 12)$ passes through the origin. Which of the following could be the value of $m$?

A. $\sqrt{6}$

B. $12$

C. $6\sqrt{2}$

D. $9$

E. $6$

56) A function $g(3) = 5$ and $g(6) = 4$. A function $f(5) = 2$ and $f(4) = 7$. What is the value of $f(g(6))$?

A. 5

B. 7

C. 8

D, 9

E. 12

57) What is the area of the following equilateral triangle if the side $AB = 8\ cm$?

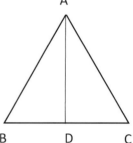

A. $16\sqrt{3}\ cm^2$

B. $8\sqrt{3}\ cm^2$

C. $\sqrt{3}\ cm^2$

D. $8\ cm^2$

E. $6\ cm^2$

58) A function $g(x)$ satisfies $g(4) = 5$ and $g(7) = 8$. A function $f(x)$ satisfies $f(5) = 18$ and $f(8) = 35$. What is the value of $f(g(7))$?

A. 12

B. 22

C. 35

D. 42

E. 46

$$(x + 2)^2 + (y - 4)^2 = 16$$

59) In the standard $(x, y)$ coordinate system plane, what is the area of the circle with the above equation?

A. $24\pi$

B. $18\pi$

C. $16\pi$

D. $\sqrt{10}$

E. $\sqrt{10}\ \pi$

60) Right triangle $ABC$ is shown below. Which of the following is true for all possible values of angle $A$ and $B$?

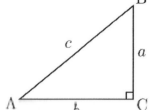

A. $tan\ A = \dfrac{a}{c}$

B. $sin\ A = \dfrac{a}{c}$

C. $cot^2 A = 0$

D. $tan\ A = 1$

E. $cos\ A = \dfrac{b}{a}$

## End of CLEP College Algebra Practice Test 2

# CLEP College Algebra Practice Tests Answer Keys

Now, it's time to review your results to see where you went wrong and what areas you need to improve.

| CLEP College Algebra Practice Test 1 | | | | | | CLEP College Algebra Practice Test 2 | | | | | |
|---|---|---|---|---|---|---|---|---|---|---|---|
| 1 | A | 21 | E | 41 | D | 1 | C | 21 | C | 41 | C |
| 2 | A | 22 | E | 42 | C | 2 | B | 22 | C | 42 | A |
| 3 | D | 23 | B | 43 | B | 3 | A | 23 | B | 43 | C |
| 4 | D | 24 | A | 44 | C | 4 | A | 24 | A | 44 | C |
| 5 | B | 25 | D | 45 | C | 5 | C | 25 | A | 45 | C |
| 6 | C | 26 | A | 46 | D | 6 | C | 26 | E | 46 | A |
| 7 | C | 27 | E | 47 | A | 7 | D | 27 | C | 47 | B |
| 8 | C | 28 | B | 48 | D | 8 | B | 28 | C | 48 | D |
| 9 | B | 29 | C | 49 | D | 9 | D | 29 | E | 49 | B |
| 10 | D | 30 | D | 50 | D | 10 | C | 30 | D | 50 | B |
| 11 | D | 31 | A | 51 | C | 11 | C | 31 | E | 51 | C |
| 12 | A | 32 | A | 52 | C | 12 | B | 32 | E | 52 | D |
| 13 | C | 33 | C | 53 | B | 13 | B | 33 | E | 53 | C |
| 14 | B | 34 | E | 54 | B | 14 | C | 34 | E | 54 | C |
| 15 | B | 35 | E | 55 | A | 15 | D | 35 | C | 55 | C |
| 16 | B | 36 | B | 56 | D | 16 | B | 36 | D | 56 | B |
| 17 | D | 37 | E | 57 | B | 17 | D | 37 | B | 57 | A |
| 18 | A | 38 | D | 58 | A | 18 | B | 38 | B | 58 | C |
| 19 | B | 39 | C | 59 | A | 19 | B | 39 | D | 59 | C |
| 20 | E | 40 | A | 60 | D | 20 | B | 40 | B | 60 | B |

# CLEP College Algebra Practice Tests Answers and Explanations

# CLEP College Algebra Practice Test 1

## Answers and Explanations

**1) Choice A is correct**

$(\frac{f}{g})(x) = \frac{f(x)}{g(x)} = \frac{2x+2}{x^2+4x}$

**2) Choice A is correct.**

The equation of a line is: $y = mx + b$, where $m$ is the slope and $b$ is the y-intercept.

First find the slope: $m = \frac{y_2-y_1}{x_2-x_1} = \frac{15 \ (-5)}{8-3} = \frac{20}{5} = 4.$     Then, we have: $y = 4x + b$

Choose one point and plug in the values of $x$ and $y$ in the equation to solve for $b$.

Let's choose the point $(3, -5)$. $y = 4x + b \rightarrow -5 = 4(3) + b \rightarrow -5 = 12 + b \rightarrow b = -17$

The equation of the line is: $y = 4x - 17$

**3) Choice D is correct**

Use FOIL method. $(5x + 2y)(2x - y) = 10x^2 - 5xy + 4xy - 2y^2 = 10x^2 - xy - 2y^2$

**4) Choice D is correct**

To solve absolute values equations, write two equations. $x - 10$ could be positive 4, or negative 4. Therefore, $x - 10 = 4 \Rightarrow x = 14$, $x - 10 = -4 \Rightarrow x = 6$. Find the product of solutions: $6 \times 14 = 84$

**5) Choice B is correct**

The equation of a line in slope intercept form is: $y = mx + b$. Solve for $y$.

$4x - 2y = 6 \Rightarrow -2y = 6 - 4x \Rightarrow y = (6 - 4x) \div (-2) \Rightarrow y = 2x - 3$. The slope is 2.

The slope of the line perpendicular to this line is: $m_1 \times m_2 = -1 \Rightarrow 2 \times m_2 = -1 \Rightarrow m_2 = -\frac{1}{2}$.

**6) Choice C is correct**

Plug in the value of $x$ and $y$. $x = 3$ and $y = -2$.

**7) Choice C is correct**

To rewrite $\frac{2+3i}{5-2i}$ in the standard form $a + bi$, multiply the numerator and denominator of $\frac{2+3i}{5-2i}$ by the conjugate, $5 + 2i$. This gives $\left(\frac{2+3i}{5-2i}\right)\left(\frac{5+2i}{5+2i}\right) = \frac{10+4i+15i+\phantom{(}^2}{5^2-(2i)^2}$. Since $i^2 = -1$, this last fraction can be rewritten as $\frac{10+4i+15i+\phantom{(}(-1)}{25-4(-1)} = \frac{4+19i}{29}$.

**8) Choice C is correct**

First find the value of $b$, and then find $f(3)$. Since $f(2) = 35$, substituting $2$ for $x$ and $35$ for $f(x)$ gives $35 = b(2)^2 + 15 = 4b + 15$. Solving this equation gives $b = 5$. Thus

$$f(x) = 5x^2 + 15, \quad f(3) = 5(3)^2 + 15 \rightarrow f(3) = 45 + 15, \ f(3) = 60$$

**9) Choice B is correct**

The diagonal of the square is 4. Let $x$ be the side. Use Pythagorean Theorem: $a^2 + b^2 = c^2$

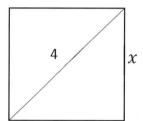

$$x^2 + x^2 = 4^2 \Rightarrow 2x^2 = 4^2 \Rightarrow 2x^2 = 16 \Rightarrow x^2 = 8 \Rightarrow x = \sqrt{8}$$

The area of the square is: $\sqrt{8} \times \sqrt{8} = 8$

**10) Choice D is correct**

Solve for the sum of five numbers.

$$\text{average} = \frac{\text{sum of terms}}{\text{number of terms}} \Rightarrow 26 = \frac{\text{sum of 5 numbers}}{5} \Rightarrow \text{sum of 5 numbers} = 26 \times 5 = 130$$

The sum of 5 numbers is 130. If a sixth number 42 is added, then the sum of 6 numbers is

$130 + 42 = 172$. The new average is: $\frac{\text{sum of 6 numbers}}{6} = \frac{172}{6} = 28.66$

**11) Choice D is correct**

The rate of construction company $= \frac{30 \text{ cm}}{1 \text{ min}} = 30 \text{ cm/min}$

Height of the wall after 40 minutes $= \frac{30 \text{ cm}}{1 \text{ min}} \times 40 \text{ min} = 1200 \text{ cm}$

Let $x$ be the height of wall, then $\frac{3}{4}x = 1200 \text{ cm} \rightarrow x = \frac{4 \times 1200}{3} \rightarrow x = 1600 \text{ cm} = 16 \, m$

**12) Choice A is correct**

$x - 2 \geq 3 \rightarrow x \geq 3 + 2 \rightarrow x \geq 5$ Or $x - 2 \leq -3 \rightarrow x \leq -3 + 2 \rightarrow x \leq -1$

Then, solution is: $x \geq 5 \ \cup \ x \leq -1$

**13) Choice C is correct**

When 5 times the number $x$ is added to 10, the result is $10 + 5x$. Since this result is equal to 35, the equation $10 + 5x = 35$ is true. Subtracting 10 from each side of $10 + 5x = 35$ gives $5x = 25$, and then dividing both sides by 5 gives $x = 5$. Therefore, 3 times $x$ added to 6, or $6 + 3x$, is equal to $6 + 3(5) = 21$.

**14) Choice B is correct**

Fining $g$ in term of $h$, simply means "solve the equation for $g$". To solve for $g$, isolate it on one side of the equation. Since $g$ is on the left-hand side, just keep it there.

Subtract both sides by $3h$. $3h + g - 3h = 8h + 4 - 3h$

And simplifying makes the equation $g = 5h + 4$, which happens to be the answer.

**15) Choice B is correct**

Isolate and solve for $x.\frac{2}{3}x + \frac{1}{6} = \frac{1}{2} \Rightarrow \frac{2}{3}x = \frac{1}{2} - \frac{1}{6} = \frac{1}{3} \Rightarrow \frac{2}{3}x = \frac{1}{3}$ .Multiply both sides by the reciprocal of the coefficient of $x$. $(\frac{3}{2})\frac{1}{3}x = \frac{1}{3}(\frac{3}{2}) \Rightarrow x = \frac{3}{6} = \frac{1}{2}$

**16) Choice B is correct**

Use simple interest formula:$I = prt$ ($I$ = interest, $p$ = principal, $r$ = rate, $t$ = time).

$I = (12,000)(0.045)(2) = 1,080$

**17) Choice D is correct**

Simplify. $7x^2y^3(2x^2y)^3 = 7x^2y^3(8x^6y^3) = 56x^8y^6$

**18) Choice E is correct**

Frist factor the function: $f(x) = x^3 + 7x^2 + 12x = x(x + 3)(x + 4)$

To find the zeros, $f(x)$ should be zero. $f(x) = x(x + 3)(x + 4) = 0$

Therefore, the zeros are: $x = 0$, $(x + 3) = 0 \Rightarrow x = -3$, $(x + 4) = 0 \Rightarrow x = -4$

**19) Choice B is correct.**

$sin^2a + cos^2a = 1$, then: $x + 1 = 3$, $x = 2$

**20) Choice E is correct.**

Solve for $x$. $\sqrt{3x} = \sqrt{y}$. Square both sides of the equation: $(\sqrt{3x})^2 = (\sqrt{y})^2 \rightarrow 3x = y \rightarrow x = \frac{y}{3}$

**21) Choice E is correct**

$g(x) = -4,$ **then** $f\big(g(x)\big) = f(-4) = 2(-4)^3 + 5(-4)^2 + 2(-4) = -128 + 80 - 8 = -56$

**22) Choice E is correct**

Use the information provided in the question to draw the shape.

Use Pythagorean Theorem: $a^2 + b^2 = c^2$

$50^2 + 120^2 = c^2 \Rightarrow 2,500 + 14,400 = c^2 \Rightarrow$

$16,900 = c^2 \Rightarrow c = 130$

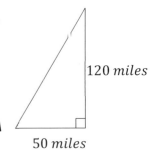

Port A

120 *miles*

50 *miles*

**23) Choice B is correct**

Plug in 104 for $F$ and then solve for $C$.

$$C = \frac{5}{9}(F - 32) \Rightarrow C = \frac{5}{9}(104 - 32) \Rightarrow C = \frac{5}{9}(72) = 40$$

**24) Choice A is correct**

The width of the rectangle is twice its length. Let $x$ be the length. Then, $width = 2x$

Perimeter of the rectangle is $2\,(width + length) = 2(2x + x) = 72 \Rightarrow 6x = 72 \Rightarrow x = 12$. Length of the rectangle is 12 meters.

**25) Choice D is correct**

$average = \frac{\text{sum of terms}}{\text{number of terms}} \Rightarrow$ (average of 6 numbers) $14 = \frac{\text{sum of numbers}}{6} \Rightarrow$ sum of 6 numbers is $14 \times 6 = 84$, (average of 4 numbers) $10 = \frac{\text{sum of numbers}}{4} \Rightarrow$ sum of 4 numbers is $10 \times 4 = 40$. $sum\ of\ 6\ numbers - sum\ of\ 4\ numbers = sum\ of\ 2\ numbers$,

$84 - 40 = 44$; average of 2 numbers $= \frac{44}{2} = 22$

**26) Choice A is correct**

First, find the number. Let $x$ be the number. Write the equation and solve for $x$. 150% of a number is 75, then: $1.5 \times x = 75 \Rightarrow x = 75 \div 1.5 = 50$, 80% of 50 is: $0.8 \times 50 = 40$

**27) Choice E is correct**

Solve for $y$. $4x - 2y = 12 \Rightarrow -2y = 12 - 4x \Rightarrow y = 2x - 6$. The slope of the line is 2.

**28) Choice B is correct**

the population is increased by 10% and 20%. 10% increase changes the population to 110% of original population. For the second increase, multiply the result by 120%.

$(1.10) \times (1.20) = 1.32 = 132\%$. 32 percent of the population is increased after two years.

**29) Choice C is correct**

The formula for the area of the circle is: $A = \pi r^2$ ,The area is $36\pi$. Therefore: $A = \pi r^2 \Rightarrow 6\pi = \pi r^2$, Divide both sides by $\pi$: $36 = r^2 \Rightarrow r = 6$. Diameter of a circle is $2 \times$ radius. Then: $Diameter = 2 \times 6 = 12$

**30) Choice D is correct**

If 20% of a number is 4, what is the number: $20\%\ of\ x = 4 \Rightarrow 0.20\,x = 4 \Rightarrow x = 4 \div 0.20 = 20$

**31) Choice A is correct**

Substituting $x$ for $y$ in first equation. $5x + 2y = 3, \qquad 5x + 2(x) = 3, \qquad 7x = 3$

Divide both side of $7x = 3$ by 3 gives $x = \dfrac{3}{7}$

**32) Choice A is correct**

There are 5 floors, $x$ rooms in each floor, and $y$ chairs per room. If you multiply 5 floors by $x$, there are $5x$ rooms in the hotel. To get the number of chairs in the hotel, multiply $5x$ by $y$. $5xy$ is the number of chairs in the hotel.

**33) Choice C is correct**

If $\beta = 3\gamma$, then multiplying both sides by 12 gives $12\beta = 36\gamma$.

$\alpha = 2\beta$, thus $\alpha = 6\gamma$. Multiply both sides of the equation by 6 gives $6\alpha = 36\gamma$.

**34) Choice E is correct**

$g(x) = -3,$ **then** $f\big(g(x)\big) = f(-3) = 2\,(-3)^3 + 5(-3)^2 + 2(-3) = -54 + 45 - 6 = -15$

**35) Choice E is correct**

Let $x$ be the width of the rectangle. Use Pythagorean Theorem:

$a^2 + b^2 = c^2$

$x^2 + 6^2 = 10^2 \Rightarrow x^2 + 36 = 100 \Rightarrow x^2 = 100 - 36 = 64 \Rightarrow x = 8$

Perimeter of the rectangle $= 2\,(length + width) = 2\,(8 + 6) = 2\,(14) = 28$

**36) Choice B is correct**

The perimeter of the trapezoid is 40.herefore, the missing side (height) is

$= 40 - 8 - 12 - 6 = 14$. Area of a trapezoid: $A = \dfrac{1}{2}\,h\,(b_1 + b_2) = \dfrac{1}{2}\,(14)\,(6 + 8) = 98$

**37) Choice E is correct**

$f\big(g(x)\big) = 2 \times \left(\dfrac{1}{x}\right)^3 + 2 = \dfrac{2}{x^3} + 2$

**38) Choice D is correct**

Use the information provided in the question to draw the shape.

Use Pythagorean Theorem: $a^2 + b^2 = c^2$

$80^2 + 150^2 = c^2 \Rightarrow 6400 + 22500 = c^2 \Rightarrow 28900 = c^2$
$\Rightarrow c = 170$

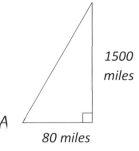

Port A

1500 miles

80 miles

**39) Choice C is correct**

Write the ratio of $5a$ to $2b$. $\frac{5a}{2b} = \frac{1}{10}$. Use cross multiplication and then simplify.

$5a \times 10 = 2b \times 1 \rightarrow 50a = 2b \rightarrow a = \frac{2b}{50} = \frac{b}{25}$

Now, find the ratio of $a$ to $b$. $\frac{a}{b} = \frac{\frac{b}{25}}{b} \rightarrow \frac{b}{25} \div b = \frac{b}{25} \times \frac{1}{b} = \frac{b}{25b} = \frac{1}{25}$

**40) Choice A is correct**

Plug in the value of $x$ in the equation and solve for $y$. $2y = \frac{2x^2}{3} + 6 \rightarrow 2y = \frac{2(9)^2}{3} + 6 \rightarrow$

$2y = \frac{2(81)}{3} + 6 \rightarrow 2y = 54 + 6 = 60 \rightarrow 2y = 60 \rightarrow y = 30$

**41) Choice D is correct**

Since $N = 6$, substitute 6 for $N$ in the equation $\frac{x-3}{5} = N$, which gives $\frac{x-3}{5} = 6$. Multiplying both sides of $\frac{x-3}{5} = 6$ by 5 gives $x - 3 = 30$ and then adding 3 to both sides of $x - 3 = 30$ then,

$x = 33$.

**42) Choice C is correct**

$b^{\frac{m}{n}} = \sqrt[n]{b^m}$ For any positive integers $m$ and $n$. Thus, $b^{\frac{3}{5}} = \sqrt[5]{b^3}$

**43) Choice B is correct**

The total number of pages read by Sara is 3 (hours she spent reading) multiplied by her rate of reading: $\frac{N pages}{hour} \times 3 hours = 3N$

Similarly, the total number of pages read by Mary is 4 (hours she spent reading) multiplied by her rate of reading: $\frac{M pages}{ho} \times 4 hours = 4M$ the total number of pages read by Sara and Mary is the sum of the total number of pages read by Sara and the total number of pages read by Mary: $3N + 4M$.

**44) Choice C is correct**

We know that: $i = \sqrt{-1} \Rightarrow i^2 = -1$

$(-4 + 9i)(3 + 5i) = -12 - 20i + 27i + 45i^2 = -12 + 7i - 45 = -57 + 7i$

**45) Choice C is correct**

First find the value of $b$, and then find $f(5)$. Since $f(2) = 35$, substuting 2 for $x$ and 35 for $f(x)$ gives $35 = b(2)^2 + 15 = 4b + 15$. Solving this equation gives $b = 5$. Thus $f(x) = 5x^2 + 15$, $f(5) = 5(5)^2 + 15 \rightarrow f(5) = 125 + 15$, $f(3) = 140$

**46) Choice D is correct**

Solving Systems of Equations by Elimination: Multiply the first equation by $(-2)$, then add it to the second equation.

$$-2(2x + 5y = 11) \atop 4x - 2y = -14 \Rightarrow {-4x - 10y = -22 \atop 4x - 2y = -14} \Rightarrow -12y = -36 \Rightarrow y = 3$$

Plug in the value of $y$ into one of the equations and solve for $x$.

$$2x + 5(3) = 11 \Rightarrow 2x + 15 = 11 \Rightarrow 2x = -4 \Rightarrow x = -2$$

**47) Choice A is correct**

Identify the input value. Since the function is in the form $f(x)$ and the question asks to calculate $f(4)$, the input value is four. $f(4) \rightarrow x = 4$, Using the function, input the desired $x$ value. Now substitute 4 in for every $x$ in the function. $f(x) = 3x^2 - 4$, $f(4) = 3(4)^2 - 4$, $f(4) = 48 - 4$, $f(4) = 44$

**48) Choice D is correct**

**Frist factor the function:** $f(x) = x^3 + 5x^2 + 6x = x(x + 2)(x + 3)$**, To find the zeros,** $f(x)$ **should be zero.** $f(x) = x(x + 2)(x + 3) = 0$**, Therefore, the zeros are:** $x = 0$, $(x + 2) = 0 \Rightarrow x = -2, (x + 3) = 0 \Rightarrow x = -3$

**49) Choice D is correct**

To simplify the fraction, multiply both numerator and denominator by $i$.

$$\frac{4-3i}{-4i} \times \frac{i}{i} = \frac{4i - 3i^2}{-4i^2}, i^2 - 1, \text{ Then: } \frac{4i-3i^2}{-4i^2} = \frac{4i-3(-1)}{-4(-1)} = \frac{4i+3}{4} = \frac{4i}{4} + \frac{3}{4} = \frac{3}{4} + i$$

**50) Choice D is correct**

The $x$-intercepts of the parabola represented by $y = x^2 - 7x + 12$ in the $xy$-plane are the values of $x$ for which $y$ is equal to 0.

The factored form of the equation, $y = (x - 3)(x - 4)$, shows that $y$ equals 0 if and only if

$x = 3$ or $x = 4$. Thus, the factored form $y = (x - 3)(x - 4)$, displays the $x$-intercepts. of the parabola as the constants 3 and 4.

**51) Choice C is correct**

If $x - a$ is a factor of $g(x)$, then $g(a)$ must equal 0. Based on the table $g(2) = 0$. Therefore, $x - 2$ must be a factor of $g(x)$.

**52) Choice C is correct**

To solve this problem first solve the equation for $c$. $\frac{c}{b} = 2$

Multiply by $b$ on both sides. Then: $b \times \frac{c}{b} = 2 \times b \rightarrow c = 2b$. Now to calculate $\frac{4b}{c}$, substitute the value for $c$ into the denominator and simplify. $\frac{4b}{c} = \frac{4b}{2b} = \frac{4}{2} = \frac{2}{1} = 2$

**53) Choice B is correct**

$x + 5 = 8 \rightarrow x = 8 - 5 = 3, 2y - 1 = 5 \rightarrow 2y = 6 \rightarrow y = 3, xy + 15 = 3 \times 3 + 15 = 24$

**54) Choice B is correct**

The equation $\frac{a-b}{b} = \frac{10}{13}$ can be rewritten as $\frac{a}{b} - \frac{b}{b} = \frac{10}{13}$, from which it follows that $\frac{a}{b} - 1 = \frac{10}{13}$, or $\frac{a}{b} = \frac{10}{13} + 1 = \frac{23}{13}$.

**55) Choice A is correct**

First write the equation in slope intercept form. Add $2x$ to both sides to get $6y = 2x + 24$. Now divide both sides by 6 to get $y = \frac{1}{3}x + 4$. The slope of this line is $\frac{1}{3}$, so any line that also has a slope of $\frac{1}{3}$ would be parallel to it. Only choice A has a slope of $\frac{1}{3}$.

**56) Choice D is correct**

$$average = \frac{sum\ of\ terms}{number\ of\ terms} \Rightarrow 20 = \frac{13 + 15 + 20 + x}{4} \Rightarrow 80 = 48 + x \Rightarrow x = 32$$

**57) Choice B is correct**

$\frac{x}{7} = \frac{y}{3} \rightarrow 7y = 3x \rightarrow y = \frac{3}{7}x$

**58) Choice A is correct**

The sum of all angles in a quadrilateral is 360 degrees. Let $x$ be the smallest angle in the quadrilateral. Then the angles are: $x, 2x, 3x, 4x$,

$x + 2x + 3x + 4x = 360 \rightarrow 10x = 360 \rightarrow x = 36$, The angles in the quadrilateral are: $36°, 72°, 108°$, and $144°$, The smallest angle is 36 degrees.

**59) Choice A is correct**

Since a box of pen costs \$3, then $3p$ Represents the cost of $p$ boxes of pen. Multiplying this number times 1.085 will increase the cost by the 8.5% for tax. Then add the \$6 shipping fee for the total: $1.085(3p) + 6$

**60) Choice D is correct**

Rate of change (growth or $x$) is 8 per week. $40 \div 5 = 8$

Since the plant grows at a linear rate, then the relationship between the height $(y)$ of the plant and number of weeks of growth $(x)$ can be written as: $y(x) = 8x$

# CLEP College Algebra Practice Test 2

## Answers and Explanations

### 1) Choice C is correct

Let $x$ be the number. Write the equation and solve for $x$. $(24 - x) \div x = 3$. Multiply both sides by $x$. $(24 - x) = 3x$, then add x both sides. $24 = 4x$, now divide both sides by 4. $x = 6$

### 2) Choice B is correct

The sum of supplement angles is 180. Let $x$ be that angle. Therefore, $x + 5x = 180$

$6x = 180$, divide both sides by 6: $x = 30$

### 3) Choice A is correct

$$x1,2 = \frac{-b \pm \sqrt{b^2 - 4ac}}{2a}; \quad ax2 + bx + c = 0$$

$x2 + 2x - 5 = 0 \Rightarrow$ then: a = 1, b = 2 and c = $-5$

$$x = \frac{-2 + \sqrt{2^2 - 4.1.-5}}{2.1} = \sqrt{6} - 1; \quad x = \frac{-2 - \sqrt{2^2 - 4.1.-5}}{2.1} = -1 - \sqrt{6}$$

### 4) Choice A is correct

*To simplify the fraction, multiply both numerator and denominator by i.*

$\frac{4 - 3i}{-4i} \times \frac{i}{i} = \frac{4i - 3i^2}{-4i^2}; \cdot i^2 - 1$, *Then:* $\frac{4i - 3i^2}{-4i^2} = \frac{4i - 3(-1)}{-4(-1)} = \frac{4i + 3}{4} = \frac{4i}{4} + \frac{3}{4} = i + \frac{3}{4}$

### 5) Choice C is correct

The sum of the two polynomials is $(4x^2 + 6x - 3) + (3x^2 - 5x + 8)$

This can be rewritten by combining like terms: $(4x^2 + 6x - 3) + (3x^2 - 5x + 8) = (4x^2 + 3x^2) + (6x - 5x) + (-3 + 8) = 7x^2 + x + 5$

### 6) Choice C is correct

Plugin the values of x in the choices provided. The points are $(1, -1), (2, -3),$ and $(3, -5)$

For $(1, -1)$ check the options provided:

A. $g(x) = 2x + 1 \rightarrow -1 = 2(1) + 1 \rightarrow -1 = 3$      This is NOT true.

B. $g(x) = 2x - 1 \rightarrow -1 = 2(1) - 1 = 1$      This is NOT true.

C. $g(x) = -2x + 1 \rightarrow -1 = 2(-1) + 1 \rightarrow -1 = -1$      This is true.

D. $g(x) = x + 2 \rightarrow -1 = 1 + 2 \rightarrow -1 = 3$      This is NOT true.

E. $g(x) = 2x + 2 \rightarrow -1 = 2(1) + 2 = 1$      This is NOT true.

**7) Choice C is correct**

Use distance formula: $Distance = Rate \times time \Rightarrow 420 = 50 \times T$, divide both sides by 50. $420 \div 50 = T \Rightarrow T = 8.4 \, hours$. Change hours to minutes for the decimal part. $0.4 \, hours = 0.4 \times 60 = 24 \, minutes$.

**8) Choice B is correct.**

Simplify the expression. $\sqrt{\frac{x^4}{4} + \frac{x^4}{16}} = \sqrt{\frac{8x^4}{16} + \frac{x^4}{16}} = \sqrt{\frac{9x^4}{16}} = \sqrt{\frac{9}{16}x^2} = \sqrt{\frac{9}{16}} \times \sqrt{x^2} = \frac{3}{4} \times x = \frac{3x}{4}$

**9) Choice D is correct**

To find the $y-$intercept of a line from its equation, put the equation in slope-intercept form:

$x - 3y = 12, -3y = -x + 12, 3y = x - 12, y = \frac{1}{3}x - 4$

The $y-$intercept is what comes after the $x$. Thus, the $y-$intercept of the line is $-4$.

**10) Choice C is correct**

Adding both side of $4a - 3 = 17$ by 3 gives $4a = 20$

Divide both side of $4a = 20$ by 4 gives $a = 5$, then $6a = 6(5) = 30$

**11) Choice E is correct**

The perimeter of the trapezoid is 54.

Therefore, the missing side (height) is $= 54 - 18 - 12 - 14 = 10$

Area of the trapezoid: $A = \frac{1}{2}h(b_1 + b_2) = \frac{1}{2}(10)(12 + 14) = 130$

**12) Choice C is correct**

Let $x$ be the number. Write the equation and solve for $x$. $\frac{2}{3} \times 18 = \frac{2}{5} \cdot x \Rightarrow \frac{2 \times 18}{3} = \frac{2x}{5}$, use cross multiplication to solve for $x$. $5 \times 36 = 2x \times 3 \Rightarrow 180 = 6x \Rightarrow x = 30$

**13) Choice B is correct**

The easiest way to solve this one is to plug the answers into the equation.

When you do this, you will see the only time $x = x^{-6}$ is when $x = 1$ or $x = 0$.

Only $x = 1$ is provided in the choices.

**14) Choice C is correct**

First find a common denominator for both of the fractions in the expression $\frac{5}{x^2} + \frac{7x-3}{x^3}$.

of $x^3$, we can combine like terms into a single numerator over the denominator:

$\frac{5x + 4}{x^3} + \frac{7x - 3}{x^3} = \frac{(5x + 4) + (7x - 3)}{x^3} = \frac{12x + 1}{x^3}$

**15) Choice D is correct**

Let's find the vertex of each choice provided:

A. $y = 3x^2 - 3$          The vertex is: $(0, -3)$

B. $y = -3x^2 + 3$         The vertex is: $(0, 3)$

C. $y = x^2 + 3x - 3$      The value of $x$ of the vertex in the equation of a quadratic in standard form is: $x = \frac{b}{2a} = \frac{3}{2}$

(The standard equation of a quadratic is: $ax^2 + bx + c = 0$)

The value of $x$ in the vertex is 3 not $\frac{-3}{2}$.

D. $y = 4(x - 3)^2 - 3$

Vertex form of a parabola equation is in form of $y = a(x - h)^2 + k$, where $(h, k)$ is the vertex. Then $h = 3$ and $k = -3$. (This is the answer)

E. $y = 4x^2 + 3x - 3$. $x = \frac{-b}{2a} = \frac{-3}{2 \times 8} = -\frac{3}{16}$. The value of $x$ in the vertex is 3 not $-\frac{3}{16}$.

**16) Choice B is correct**

Use the information provided in the question to draw the shape.

Use Pythagorean Theorem: $a^2 + b^2 = c^2$

$40^2 + 30^2 = c^2 \Rightarrow 1600 + 900 = c^2 \Rightarrow 2500 = c^2 \Rightarrow c = 50$

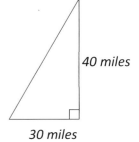

40 miles

30 miles

**17) Choice D is correct**

To find the average of three numbers even if they're algebraic expressions, add them up and divide by 3. Thus, the average equals: $\frac{(4x+2)+(-6x-5)+(8x+2)}{3} = \frac{6x-1}{3} = 2x - \frac{1}{3}$

**18) Choice B is correct**

If the score of Mia was 60, therefore the score of Ava is 30. Since, the score of Emma was half as that of Ava, therefore, the score of Emma is 15.

**19) Choice B is correct**

Let $x$ be the smallest number. Then, these are the numbers: $x, x + 1, x + 2, x + 3, x + 4$

$average = \frac{\text{sum of terms}}{\text{number of terms}} \Rightarrow 38 = \frac{x+(x+1)+(x+2)+(x+3)+(x+4)}{5} \Rightarrow 38 = \frac{5x+10}{5} \Rightarrow 190 = 5x + 10 \Rightarrow 180 = 5x \Rightarrow x = 36$

**20) Choice B is correct.**

Let $x$ be the number of adult tickets and $y$ be the number of student tickets. Then:

$x + y = 12$, $12.50x + 7.50y = 125$

Use elimination method to solve this system of equation. Multiply the first equation by $-7.5$ and add it to the second equation. $-7.5(x + y = 12)$,     $-7.5x - 7.5y = -90$, $12.50x + 7.50y = 125$. $5x = 35$, $x = 7$

There are 7 adult tickets and 5 student tickets.

**21) Choice C is correct**

Write the ratio of $5a$ to $2b$. $\frac{5a}{2b} = \frac{1}{10}$

Use cross multiplication and then simplify. $5a \times 10 = 2b \times 1 \rightarrow 50a = 2b \rightarrow a = \frac{2b}{50} = \frac{b}{25}$

Now, find the ratio of $a$ to $b$. $\frac{a}{b} = \frac{\frac{b}{25}}{b} \rightarrow \frac{b}{25} \div b = \frac{b}{25} \times \frac{1}{b} = \frac{b}{25b} = \frac{1}{25}$

**22) Choice C is correct**

4% of the volume of the solution is alcohol. Let $x$ be the volume of the solution.

Then: $4\%\ of\ x = 24\ ml \Rightarrow 0.04\ x = 24 \Rightarrow x = 24 \div 0.04 = 600$

**23) Choice B is correct**

$average = \frac{sum\ of\ terms}{number\ of\ terms}$, The sum of the weight of all girls is: $18 \times 60 = 1080\ kg$, The sum of the weight of all boys is: $32 \times 62 = 1984\ kg$, The sum of the weight of all students is: $1080 + 1984 = 3064\ kg$, average $= \frac{3064}{50} = 61.28$

**24) Choice A is correct**

Plug in the value of $x$ in the equation and solve for $y$.

$2y = \frac{2x^2}{3} + 6 \rightarrow 2y = \frac{2(9)^2}{3} + 6 \rightarrow 2y = \frac{2(81)}{3} + 6 \rightarrow 2y = 54 + 6 = 60$

$2y = 60 \rightarrow y = 30$

**25) Choice A is correct**

Since a box of pen costs $3, then $3p$ Represents the cost of $p$ boxes of pen.

Multiplying this number times 1.085 will increase the cost by the 8.5% for tax.

Then add the $6 shipping fee for the total: $1.085(3p) + 6$

**26) Choice E is correct**

$average = \frac{sum\ of\ terms}{number\ of\ terms} \Rightarrow 18 = \frac{13 + 15 + 20 +}{4} \Rightarrow 72 = 48 + x \Rightarrow x = 24$

**27) Choice C is correct**

Let $x$ be the original price. If the price of the sofa is decreased by 25% to \$420, then:
$75\% \; of \; x = 420 \Rightarrow 0.75x = 420 \Rightarrow x = 420 \div 0.75 = 560$

**28) Choice C is correct**

Use simple interest formula: $I = prt$, ($I$ = interest, $p$ = principal, $r$ = rate, $t$ = time)

$I = (8,000)(0.045)(5) = 1,800$

**29) Choice E is correct**

$(4.2 \times 10^6) \times (2.6 \times 10^{-5}) = (4.2 \times 2.6) \times (10^6 \times 10^{-5}) = 10.92 \times (10^{6 + (-5)}) = 1.092 \times 10^2$

**30) Choice D is correct**

Rate of change (growth or $x$) is 15 per week. $45 \div 3 = 15$

Since the plant grows at a linear rate, then the relationship between the height ($y$) of the plant and number of weeks of growth ($x$) can be written as: $y(x) = 15x$

**31) Choice E is correct**

Simplify: $4(x + 1) = 6(x - 4) + 20, 4x + 4 = 6x - 24 + 20, 4x + 4 = 6x - 4$

Subtract $4x$ from both sides: $4 = 2x - 4$, Add 4 to both sides: $8 = 2x, 4 = x$

**32) Choice E is correct**

Use distributive property: $2x(4 + 2y) = 8x + 4xy = 4xy + 8x$

**33) Choice E is correct**

$y = 4ab + 3b^3$, plug in the values of $a$ and $b$ in the equation: $a = 2$ and $b = 3$,

$y = 4(2)(3) + 3(3)^3 = 24 + 3(27) = 24 + 81 = 105$

**34) Choice E is correct**

Based on corresponding members from two matrices, we get: $\begin{cases} 2x = x + 3y - 5 \\ 4x = 2y - 10 \end{cases} \rightarrow \begin{cases} x - 3y = -5 \\ 4x - 2y = 10 \end{cases}$

Multiply first equation by $-4$. $\begin{cases} -4x + 12y = 20 \\ 4x - 2y = 10 \end{cases} \rightarrow$ add two equations.

$10y = 30 \rightarrow y = 3 \rightarrow x = 4 \rightarrow x \times y = 12$

**35) Choice C is correct.**

To solve for $f(3g(P))$, first, find $3g(p)$: $g(x) = log_3 x \rightarrow g(p) = log_3 p \rightarrow 3g(p) =$

$3log_3 p = log_3 p^3$. Now, find $f(3g(p))$: $f(x) = 3^x \rightarrow f(log_3 p^3) = 3^{log_3 p^3}$

Logarithms and exponentials with the same base cancel each other. This is true because logarithms and exponentials are inverse operations. Then: $f(log_3 p^3) = 3^{log_3 p^3} = p^3$

**36) Choice D is correct**

A. $f(x) = x^2 - 5$    if      $x = 1 \rightarrow f(1) = (1)^2 - 5 = 1 - 5 = -4 \neq 5$

B. $f(x) = x^2 - 1$    if      $x = 1 \rightarrow f(1) = (1)^2 - 1 = 1 - 1 = 0 \neq 5$

C. $f(x) = \sqrt{x + 2}$    if      $x = 1 \rightarrow f(1) = \sqrt{1 + 2} = \sqrt{3} \neq 5$

D. $f(x) = \sqrt{x} + 4$    if      $x = 1 \rightarrow f(1) = \sqrt{1} + 4 = 5$

E. $f(x) = \sqrt{x} + 6$    if      $x = 1 \rightarrow f(1) = \sqrt{1} + 6 \neq 5$

**37) Choice B is correct**

Plug in each pair of number in the equation:

A. $(2, 1)$:          $2(2) + 4(1) = 8$

B. $(-1, 3)$:       $2(-1) + 4(3) = 10$

C. $(-2, 2)$:       $2(-2) + 4(2) = 4$

D. $(2, 2)$:          $2(2) + 4(2) = 12$

E. $(2, 8)$:          $2(2) + 4(8) = 36$

Only Choice B is correct.

**38) Choice B is correct.**

A linear equation is a relationship between two variables, $x$ and $y$, and can be written in the form of $y = mx + b$. A non-proportional linear relationship takes on the form $y = mx + b$, where $b \neq 0$ and its graph is a line that does not cross through the origin. Only in graph B, the line does not pass through the origin

**39) Choice D is correct**

The relationship among all sides of special right triangle

$30° - 60° - 90°$ is provided in this triangle:

In this triangle, the opposite side of $30°$ angle is half of the hypotenuse.

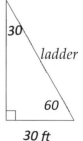

Draw the shape of this question:

The ladder is the hypotenuse. Therefore, the ladder is $60 \, ft$

**40) Choice B is correct.**

By definition, the sine of any acute angle is equal to the cosine of its complement.

Since, angle A and B are complementary angles, therefore: $sin\ A\ =\ cos\ B$

**41) Choice C is correct**

Method 1: Plugin the values of $x$ and $y$ provided in the options into both equations.

A. $(1, 3)$       $x + y \quad 0 \quad 1 \quad 3 \neq 0$

B. $(5, 4)$       $x + y = 0 \rightarrow 5 + 4 \neq 0$

C. $(4, -4)$      $x + y = 0 \rightarrow 4 + (-4) = 0$

D. $(4, -6)$      $x + y = 0 \rightarrow 4 + (-6) \neq 0$

E. $(2, -6)$      $x + y = 0 \rightarrow 2 + (-6) \neq 0$

Only option C is correct.

Method 2: Multiplying each side of $x + y = 0$ by 2 gives $2x + 2y = 0$. Then, adding the corresponding side of $2x + 2y = 0$ and $4x - 2y = 24$ gives $6x = 24$. Dividing each side of $6x = 24$ by 6 gives $x = 4$. Finally, substituting 4 for $x$ in $x + y = 0$, or $y = -4$. Therefore, the solution to the given system of equations is $(4, -4)$.

**42) Choice A is correct**

If $f(x) = 3x + 4(x + 1) + 2$, then find $f(3x)$ by substituting $3x$ for every $x$ in the function. This gives: $f(3x) = 3\ (3x) + 4(3x + 1) + 2$

It simplifies to: $f(3x) = 3\ (3x) + 4(3x + 1) + 2 = 9x + 12x + 4 + 2 = 21x + 6$

**43) Choice C is correct**

First, find the equation of the line. All lines through the origin are of the form $y = mx$, so the equation is $y = \frac{2}{3}x$. Of the given choices, only choice C $(9,6)$, satisfies this equation:

$$y = \frac{2}{3}x \rightarrow 6 = \frac{2}{3}(9) = 6$$

**44) Choice C is correct**

$(3n^2 + 4n + 6) - (2n^2 - 5)$. Add like terms together: $3n^2 - 2n^2 = n^2$

$4n$ doesn't have like terms. $6 - (-5) = 11$

Combine these terms into one expression to find the answer: $n^2 + 4n + 11$

**45) Choice C is correct**

You can find the possible values of $a$ and $b$ in $(ax + 4)(bx + 3)$ by using the given equation $a + b = 7$ and finding another equation that relates the variables $a$ and $b$. Since $(ax + 4)(bx + 3) = 10x^2 + cx + 12$, expand the left side of the equation to obtain

$abx^2 + 4bx + 3ax + 12 = 10x^2 + cx + 12$

Since $ab$ is the coefficient of $x^2$ on the left side of the equation and 10 is the coefficient of $x^2$ on the right side of the equation, it must be true that $ab = 10$

The coefficient of $x$ on the left side is $4b + 3a$ and the coefficient of $x$ in the right side is c. Then: $4b + 3a = c$, $\quad a + b = 7$, then: $a = 7 - b$

Now, plug in the value of a in the equation $ab = 10$. Then:

$ab = 10 \rightarrow (7 - b)b = 10 \rightarrow 7b - b^2 = 10$

Add $-7b + b^2$ both sides. Then: $b^2 - 7b + 10 = 0$

Solve for b using the factoring method. $b^2 - 7b + 10 = 0 \rightarrow (b - 5)(b - 2) = 0$

Thus, either $b = 2$ and $a = 5$, or $b = 5$ and $a = 2$. If $b = 2$ and $a = 5$, then

$4b + 3a = c \rightarrow 4(2) + 3(5) = c \rightarrow c = 23$. If $5 = 2$ and $a = 2$, then, $4b + 3a = c \rightarrow 4(5) + 3(2) = c \rightarrow c = 26$. $\qquad$ Therefore, the two possible values for $c$ are 23 and 26.

**46) Choice A is correct**

To rewrite $\dfrac{1}{\frac{1}{x-6}+\frac{1}{x+4}}$, first simplify $\dfrac{1}{x-6} + \dfrac{1}{x+4}$.

$\dfrac{1}{x-6} + \dfrac{1}{x+4} = \dfrac{1(x+4)}{(x-6)(x+4)} + \dfrac{1(x-5)}{(x+4)(x-6)} = \dfrac{(x+4)+(x-6)}{(x+4)(x-6)}$

Then: $\dfrac{1}{\frac{1}{x-6}+\frac{1}{x+4}} = \dfrac{1}{\frac{(x+4)+(x-6)}{(x+4)(x-6)}} = \dfrac{(x-6)(x+4)}{(x-6)+(x+4)}$. (Remember, $\dfrac{1}{\frac{1}{x}} = x$)

This result is equivalent to the expression in choice A.

**47) Choice B is correct**

Since $(0, 0)$ is a solution to the system of inequalities, substituting 0 for $x$ and 0 for $y$ in the given system must result in two true inequalities. After this substitution, $y < a - x$ becomes $0 < a$, and $y > x + b$ becomes $0 > b$. Hence, $a$ is positive and $b$ is negative. Therefore, $a > b$.

**48) Choice D is correct**

First find the slope of the line using the slope formula. $m = \frac{y_2 - y_1}{x_2 - x_1}$

Substituting in the known information. $(x_1, y_1) = (2, 4), \quad (x_2, y_2) = (4, 5)$

$m = \frac{5-4}{4-2} = \frac{1}{2}$

Now the slope to find the equation of the line passing through these points. $y = mx + b$

Choose one of the points and plug in the values of $x$ and $y$ in the equation to solve for $b$.

Let's choose point $(4, 5)$. Then: $y = mx + b \rightarrow 5 = \frac{1}{2}(4) + b \rightarrow 5 = 2 + b \rightarrow b = 5 - 2 = 3$

The equation of the line is: $y = \frac{1}{2}x + 3$

Now, plug in the points provided in the choices into the equation of the line.

A. $(9, 9)$ $\quad\quad y = \frac{1}{2}x + 3 \rightarrow 9 = \frac{1}{2}(9) + 3 \rightarrow 9 = 7.5$ This is NOT true.

B. $(9, 6)$ $\quad\quad y = \frac{1}{2}x + 3 \rightarrow 6 = \frac{1}{2}(9) + 3 \rightarrow 6 = 7.5$ This is NOT true.

C. $(6, 9)$ $\quad\quad y = \frac{1}{2}x + 3 \rightarrow 9 = \frac{1}{2}(6) + 3 \rightarrow 9 = 6$ $\quad$ This is NOT true.

D. $(6, 6)$ $\quad\quad y = \frac{1}{2}x + 3 \rightarrow 6 = \frac{1}{2}(6) + 3 \rightarrow 6 = 6$ $\quad$ This is true!

E. $(0, 9)$ $\quad\quad y = \frac{1}{2}x + 3 \rightarrow 9 = \frac{1}{2}(0) + 3 \rightarrow 9 = 3$ $\quad$ This is NOT true.

Therefore, the only point from the choices that lies on the line is $(6, 6)$.

**49) Choice B is correct**

The input value is 4. Then: $x = 4$

$f(x) = x^2 - 3x \rightarrow f(4) = 4^2 - 3(4) = 16 - 12 = 4$

**50) Choice B is correct**

To solve this problem, first recall the equation of a line: $y = mx + b$

Where $m = slope$. $y = y - intercept$

Remember that slope is the rate of change that occurs in a function and that the $y-$intercept is the $y$ value corresponding to $x = 0$. Since the height of John's plant is 6 inches tall when he gets it. Time (or $x$) is zero. The plant grows 4 inches per year. Therefore, the rate of change of the plant's height is 4. The $y-$intercept represents the starting height of the plant, which is 6 inches.

**51) Choice C is correct**

Multiplying each side of $\frac{3}{x} = \frac{12}{x-9}$ by $x(x - 9)$ gives $3(x - 9) = 12(x)$, distributing the 3 over the values within the parentheses yields $x - 9 = 4x$ or $x = -3$.

Therefore, the value of $\frac{x}{6} = \frac{-3}{6} = -\frac{1}{2}$.

**52) Choice D is correct**

The equation of a circle can be written as $(x - h)^2 + (y - k)^2 = r^2$

where $(h, k)$ are the coordinates of the center of the circle and $r$ is the radius of the circle. Since the coordinates of the center of the circle are $(0, 4)$, the equation is $x^2 + (y - 4)^2 = r^2$, where $r$ is the radius. The radius of the circle is the distance from the center $(0, 4)$, to the given endpoint of a radius, $\left(\frac{5}{3}, 6\right)$. By the distance formula,

$r^2 = \left(\frac{5}{3} - 0\right)^2 + (6 - 4)^2 = \frac{61}{9}$

Therefore, an equation of the given circle is $x^2 + (y - 4)^2 = \frac{61}{9}$

**53) Choice C is correct**

To solve for $\cos A$ first identify what is known. The question states that $\Delta ABC$ is a right triangle whose $n\angle B = 90°$ and $\sin C = \frac{2}{3}$. It is important to recall that any triangle has a sum of interior angles that equals 180 degrees. Therefore, to calculate $\cos A$ use the complimentary angles identify of trigonometric function. $\cos A = \cos(90 - C)$, Then: $\cos A = \sin C$

For complementary angles, *sin* of one angle is equal to *cos* of the other angle. $\cos A = \frac{2}{3}$

**54) Choice C is correct**

In order to figure out what the equation of the graph is, fist find the vertex. From the graph we can determine that the vertex is at $(1,2)$. We can use vertex form to solve for the equation of this graph. Recall vertex form, $y = a(x - h)^2 + k$, where $h$ is the $x$ coordinate of the vertex, and $k$ is the $y$ coordinate of the vertex. Plugging in our values, you get $= a(x - 1)^2 + 2$, To solve for $a$, we need to pick a point on the graph and plug it into the equation. Let's pick $(-1, 10)$, $10 = a(-1 - 1)^2 + 2$

$10 = a(-2)^2 + 2$, $10 = 4a + 2$, $8 = 4a$, $a = 2$

Now the equation is : $y = 2(x - 1)^2 + 2$

Let's expand this, $y = 2(x^2 - 2x + 1) + 2$, $y = 2x^2 - 4x + 2 + 2$

$y = 2x^2 - 4x + 4$. The equation in Choice C is the same.

**55) Choice C is correct**

The line passes through the origin, $(6, m)$ and $(m, 12)$. Any two of these points can be used to find the slope of the line. Since the line passes through $(0, 0)$ and $(6, m)$, the slope of the line is equal to $\frac{m - 0}{6 - 0} = \frac{m}{6}$. Similarly, since the line passes through $(0, 0)$ and $(m, 12)$, the slope of the line is equal to $\frac{12 - 0}{m - 0} = \frac{12}{m}$. Since each expression gives the slope of the same line, it must be true that $\frac{m}{6} = \frac{12}{m}$, Using cross multiplication gives

$\frac{m}{6} = \frac{12}{m} \rightarrow m^2 = 72 \rightarrow m = \pm\sqrt{72} = \pm\sqrt{36 \times 2} = \pm\sqrt{36} \times \sqrt{2} = \pm 6\sqrt{2}$

**56) Choice B is correct**

It is given that $g(6) = 4$. Therefore, to find the value of $f(g(6))$, then $f(g(6)) = f(4) = 7$

**57) Choice A is correct**

Area of the triangle is: $\frac{1}{2} AD \times BC$ and AD is perpendicular to $BC$. Triangle $ADC$ is a $30° - 60° - 90°$ right triangle. The relationship among all sides of right triangle $30° - 60° - 90°$ is provided in the following triangle: In this triangle, the opposite side of $30°$ angle is half of the hypotenuse. And the opposite side of $60°$ is opposite of $30° \times \sqrt{3}$

$CD = 4$, then $AD = 4 \times \sqrt{3}$

Area of the triangle $ABC$ is: $\frac{1}{2} AD \times BC = \frac{1}{2} 4\sqrt{3} \times 8 = 16\sqrt{3}$

**58) Choice C is correct**

It is given that $g(7) = 8$. Therefore, to find the value of $f(g(7))$, substitute 8 for $g(7)$. $f(g(7)) = f(8) = 35$.

**59) Choice C is correct**

The equation of a circle in standard form is: $(x - h)^2 + (y - k)^2 = r^2$, where $r$ is the radius of the circle. In this circle the radius is 4. $r^2 = 16 \rightarrow r = 4$, $(x + 2)^2 + (y - 4)^2 = 16$

Area of a circle: $A = \pi r^2 = \pi(4)^2 = 16\pi$

**60) Choice B is correct**

By definition, the sine of any acute angle is: $sin\,A = \frac{opposite}{adjacent} = \frac{a}{c}$. Only choice B is correct.

**"Effortless Math" Publications**

Effortless Math authors' team strives to prepare and publish the best quality Mathematics learning resources to make learning Math easier for all. We hope that our publications help you or your student Math in an effective way.

We all in Effortless Math wish you good luck and successful studies!

Effortless Math Authors

# www.EffortlessMath.com

... So Much More Online!

✓ FREE Math lessons

✓ More Math learning books!

✓ Mathematics Worksheets

✓ Online Math Tutors

**Need a PDF version of this book?**

Visit www.EffortlessMath.com

**Visit www.EffortlessMath.com**

**for Online Math Practice**

# Receive the PDF version of this book or get another FREE book!

**Thank you for using our Book!**

**Do you LOVE this book?**

**Then, you can get the PDF version of this book or another book absolutely FREE!**

Please email us at:

## info@EffortlessMath.com

for details.

Made in the USA
Columbia, SC
30 October 2020

23755401R00111